Finding the "Why in Graeagle

Whimsical Mountain Tales and Shameless Lies...

Terri —
... and a daisy for you!
Love, Paul

Paul Bianco

Finding the "Why" in Graeagle

Whimsical Mountain Tales and Shameless Lies...

Paul Bianco

ISBN 10: 0-9789177-0-7
ISBN 13: 978-0-9789177-0-8
First printing 2007

Published by:
Paul Bianco
P.O. Box 1001
Graeagle, CA 96103
530-836-0539
Cover Art: Ruthan McFarland Hudson, Graeagle
Printing: ECPrinting – www.ecprinting.com

Printed in the United States of America

Acknowledgements

My talented and compassionate camp mates during this "get off the trail" excursion have assured me they will sue for defamation if named.

So what...

Terri Keller smiled at the rough notes and quickly started a sparkling campfire.

Brandon Rose pointed out Orion and taught me how to straighten bent nails without scarring the wood.

Paula Wilson located the secret clear running waters and laughed at the thunder with me.

Thank you, my friends---

Thank you.

Introduction

Writing Art:

I don't know how to write. I don't know the rules. I don't know the difference between a pronoun and a run-on sentence. And I don't care.

I bolt words together just the way I like them and leave it at that. Sometimes they just splatter about like oil paint outside the frame. That's O.K. with me.

Others can corral with commas and diagram to unsplit infinitives and strive for precise mechanics. I'll set my large, wet, multi-colored canvas on the ground, and with a little boy's joy, pedal my bicycle through it.

Hope you have a good time, too.

Contents

Two Bits an Egg

Gladys ran the Pine Cone Cafe — No, I mean she *really* ran the cafe!

She was a big grandma-type with an oversized gingham Nebraska-style apron that seemed to exaggerate her massive arms.

It was a one-woman show in a narrow old soda fountain-like, counter only, sit down, fill-'er-up cafe.

She dealt with loggers mostly, and log truck drivers. The show started at three o'clock in the morning and stopped after breakfast. Her show.

The twelve mismatched vinyl-covered counter stools were always filled with friends and the sons of those whom she had known for many years. An exclusive working class, members only, cafe.

It wasn't a tourist place and those who haphazardly stumbled in — realizing they were in well over their heads — quickly stumbled out. It was her show for the men she cared about.

There never had been a menu, never a price and even the cafe sign outside the door that had fallen years ago had never been replaced. Just eat what she was cooking, put some money on the counter and consider yourself lucky if she ever gave you change.

Breakfast had always consisted of whatever Gladys felt like cooking, which rather than being gracefully served seemed to make a counter-pounding landing.

A massive platter of lemon eggs and goat cheese, deep fried onions and pepper grilled pork chops or aged steaks, homemade sage sausage, and oak-smoked bacon and a second large plate of spicy potatoes and oil, dill and garlic tomatoes, and extra sour, sour dough biscuits with thick cream gravy. Gallons of magnificent "secret recipe" coffee and an apple or brownie was added to the lunch pail.

Yep, this was breakfast at the Pine Cone Cafe. The old boys knew each other well and knew that the morning pre-work talk would be light and fun, as only great ribbing and badgering can be.

But nobody messed with Gladys. Anyone could torment the logger who had dropped a tree on his truck, and anyone could tease the trucker who had high-centered on a log, but nobody had ever teased Gladys!

All knew, but none ever made mention that she was the one who freely fed the old shingle splitter living in a shed at the end of the road. His days of going into the mountains were over. She didn't want anyone to know. She didn't want anyone to think that she was soft, and no one wanted to piss her off.

To Gladys it wasn't a family cafe; it was a cafe for her family. Over the years, she had hoped never to go to another logger's funeral. She had already lost too many members…too many too close to home. On a couple of occasions bodies mangled beyond recognition had made the last trip into town wrapped in a tarp and strapped onto a load of logs.

The loggers in the mountains had to deal with high-line cables that could stretch and snap and whip and cut a man in half. They adjusted to the leg-breaking attempts of devil logs that chose to roll while being limbed and bucked, log decks that tumbled for no reason and chokers that came unset. Chain saw buck-backs and leaners that can kill and those trees that twist and split and kick butt-up into a ghostly high-back barber's chair create a maybe-or-maybe-not splintered pitchy tombstone. The loggers battled against brittle snags and crotchety schoolmarms and camouflaged overhead widow makers.

It's just that, more often than thought, loggers don't die of old age.

Every morning, when her survivors rallied at the Pine Cone Cafe, Gladys would start them right with an unspoken "see you tomorrow" wish. As old as they might be, these were her kids — tough, dirty, just-tryin'-to-make-a-livin' kids but, God, please let them come back in the morning. The men were honored by her rawhide respect for them, few others had any idea of just how far into the mountains they took their chances. But she did and they knew it.

It was more than breakfast that she served up. It might have been something special about men and mountains and machines as opposed to her thoughts about the soft-handed designer-wearing types that had resort reservations with rental cars, on-demand babysitters and arrogant "wish you were here" postcards. When these boys were in the mountains their postcards might have said, "Glad you're NOT here."

Occasionally, an uninformed or ill-advised tourist happened into the Pine Cone Cafe. The locals stopped joking among themselves, and silence filled the air as they braced for the impending calamity.

They had seen this before. One tourist who mistakenly asked for a menu was escorted with a threatening spatula to the door. Another, having successfully made it through his first cup of coffee, unknowingly committed the capital crime of tapping his empty cup on the counter, signaling, so he thought, a request for a refill. He had his cup taken away and the hot new coffee stains on his pants prompted him to voluntarily exit.

Another too-well-dressed tourist, after his disingenuous comments about breakfast, wore most of his biscuits and gravy out onto the sidewalk in search of a Laundromat.

Gladys really ran the Pine Cone Cafe, but the older loggers and truckers knew and loved the drill. They ran their show in the mountains and she ran hers in the cafe. She would try not to smile and try not to pick on the one who was being teased that day, yet she always had a grand time as the game was being played on another one of her boys. The fun of watching just who was going to be the next to take the not-so-lighthearted jesting and subsequent fall was her morning entertainment.

Some would do most anything to avoid becoming the morning target of a free-for-all tease. One sleepy young logger, having stumbled late out of bed at 4:00 a.m. to the sound of an impatient truck horn, grabbed what he thought were his best pair of corks from the porch. With one hand on his yet-to-be-buckled pants, he had thrown the tall, steel-toed, spiked logging boots into the back of the quickly-leaving crew truck and jumped into the cab for the long ride to the cut. He wondered if perhaps he should have missed the truck rather than missing breakfast at the Pine Cone Cafe. Work was important but so was breakfast and one without the other seemed to be as useless as getting the bigger half of nothing.

Too late now, just deal with the draw, and hope the noise of the chainsaw might cover the growl in his empty belly. Soon he would try to count ahead just how many trees until lunch.

At the landing, his "Oh Shit!" discovery was that, in his haste, he had loaded two left boots.

His options were limited. He could work all day in his socks only. Not a fun-filled prospect but the even greater hardship would be that it would be so obvious to the other loggers. He would surely have to endure the painful suffering the next morning at the hands of his co-workers as he would become the newest defenseless member appointed to the hot seat at the cafe.

The second option seemed less perilous. Perhaps after removing his thick right sock he could work all day, inconspicuously, in two left boots. Just wear the boots with a stoic "nothing-is-wrong" purpose and hope no one spotted his foolhardy mistake, a low-cost, all-saving attempt to avoid imminent, outrageous ridicule.

Buried in the truck somewhere in the tangled mess of cables and chokers, chains and binders, snatch blocks and come-alongs, bar oil and falling wedges, chunks of pitchy cedar to start the slash burns, chainsaws needing repair and those beyond repair, all covered in grease and sawdust, rust and mud, was probably an extra set of corks.

Even looking for them would have tipped off to the others his predicament and brought about his downfall. He could imagine tomorrow's breakfast and the impending "can't tell right from left" thrashing he would receive. Someone would attempt to put a big grease pen "R" on the back of his right hand. Another would suggest that he have Erna, the water truck beauty, lay out his clothes the night before. They would laugh at the prospect of him showing up in a perfectly matched set of well-oiled corks and an extra large, lace nighty.

One would surely point out that since he only had two sets of corks, he should always grab three boots thereby insuring himself a workable right and left pair. Of course another would insist that in order to maintain an even wear pattern, he must follow up with a day of wearing two right boots. Still another would join in with some giggled theory about how two rights unmake a wrong.

All day long he jumped and cut from log to log in his two left boots. Considering the alternative, the boots felt fine.

Later, he smiled to himself as he limped back to his cabin knowing that his undiscovered story would remain untold. He then pulled off his wrong-footed boot and wondered, as he eased into the soothing hot bathtub, at the swollen ego price he had paid. "Pride comes before a fall," or something like that, he wasn't sure just what.

He looked forward to breakfast the next morning at the Pine Cone Cafe when he would heartily, mercilessly, join in the teasing of anyone who hadn't been so calculating.

Gladys had a simple policy, the one who suffered the most abrasive ridicule during breakfast was given the "Sympathy Egg." It would be packed, carefully, into the lunch pail for the high-on-a-mountain midday break.

Her not-so-subtle joke was that if she felt compassion for the recipient of the verbal thrashing during the morning saga, the reward would be that the egg was a sympathetic hardboiled consolation added to lunch.

If, on the other hand, the self-inflicted plight and subsequent foolish defense fell short of having earned the much coveted sympathy, a raw egg was the just reward.

Most mornings started with yesterday's "Egg Man" proudly reporting that the well deserved trophy had, indeed, been hardboiled. Only Gladys knew the truth and she wouldn't tell anyone, but lying meant that receiving change for your breakfast was absolutely out of the question.

Some had paid dearly for the appearance of having Gladys on their side.

The following day, it was the young logger who started the next round of teasing when he quietly asked a trucker, "This coffee taste okay to you?" He was impudent, somewhat foolish and somewhat puffed up with himself over what he had gotten away with the day before. The trucker, realizing that the game had begun, picked up the bait, didn't say a word, just waved off his 18-year traditional, four-cup-a-day refill. All had wanted to tease Gladys, but none ever had the courage to begin. The young logger had opened the gate and soon the others would rush in.

One by one they almost silently passed the word, "How's that coffee taste to you?" Not with a wink or an elbow, just a simple "here starts a game" nod. Out on the sidewalk, as one left and another arrived, the questions were the same and sly smiles were shared.

It was Logger Jim, for twenty-two years a three-cup-a-day man, who raised the bar when he asked, early on, if perhaps this day, for what was probably the first time in his life, he couldn't have hot chocolate. It almost hit the fan.

The word was handed off all day long and into the second day as some said that "just water" would do and others chokingly downed milk. One Kenworth driver was tempted, but withheld what would have been way too obvious, the thought of asking for tea. On the third day they all neglected to bring in their old dented thermoses to be filled.

Gladys stomped and pouted and sampled. She tasted and smelled and checked the power to the old coffee maker. She scrutinized the filters as pot after pot steam cleaned the drain.

The coffee salesman, fearing that he was going to be "good to the last drop," began yelping in agony at the pulling and pinching of his ear, as he swore that nothing was wrong and nothing had changed.

The County, having dealt with Gladys before, sent two water inspectors, on what normally would be a four-day awaited appointment, within hours to certify that all was well with the well water.

She had always over-served and under priced and evenly threatened her way to total control and this undermined everything. Gladys ran the show at the Pine Cone Cafe and nothing could be allowed to infringe upon her domain.

It was on the fourth day that all the loggers realized the caper had gone too far. Not that they wanted to stop the charade due to any moral code, it was just the fear that when it was ultimately discovered, "hell to pay" would be a bargain.

The one who would be the first to blow the cover would not only have to deal with the wrath of Gladys, but also with all the others who would want payback for suffering the collateral damage they surely would incur.

No one ever spoke a word. No one ever said the coffee was good. That would have been too obvious and would have lit the fuse. Just slowly they eased back into the ritual. One by one they all started drinking their coffee again as if there was nothing wrong, which, of course, there wasn't. Except Bill. The Peterbilt driver, a 24-year veteran of the Pine Cone Cafe, who had been out on a burn for seven days, had heard that the game was on but hadn't heard it had been called off due to thunder storms likely to occur at any moment.

Subtle "save us all, don't try to steal third base" signs from his cafe buddies apparently glanced off without effect as he asked for orange juice.

Gladys, her hands filled with eggs, froze in mid-omelet. Her broad back to the boys seemed to suffer a quake as the all-consuming discovery slowly settled in that this time she had become the target.

Peterbilt Bill, having taken his usual place at the end of the long narrow counter, furthest from the door, had little idea that the scales had tipped as

Gladys rotated toward him, her large hands filled with large eggs.

Almost instantly, the noisy cafe became absolutely silent as she casually stared at her hands and picked up two more eggs.

She held her head up high and in a low voice, some would later say seemed almost polite, said in an all knowing "the game is over" tone, that for two-bits he wouldn't make it to the door.

None of the loggers and drivers filling the old cafe that morning said a word or even looked at one another as each quietly reached into his suspendered trousers for a quarter. One with only a dollar bill didn't bother looking for change.

The quarters eased, not slapped, their way onto the formica counter top as all, like some synchronized swimming team, took to duck and cover.

Peterbilt Bill gave his best "what did I do?" look as he realized that what might have been the saving interference of his counter-mates had quickly disappeared as they all grabbed for the floor like bottom feeders.

He hesitated for just a second; it only took that long for him to go from "she wouldn't" to a full sprint.

Most say that there were eight hits and two misses. One hit took off his Merle Haggard hat, while another nailed his knuckles as he lunged and grabbed for the door. One miss hit the "we reserve the right to refuse service" sign which had always seemed to be an understatement. Most caught him dead center with machine gun precision.

When the firing range had cleared, all ducking patrons resumed their slack-jawed "wonder what that was about" look of innocence. Some took up napkins and towels to clean up the misses in an attempt to substantiate their "it's not my fault" position.

Gladys, the matron saint of the Pine Cone Cafe, calmly walked the length of the counter collecting all the quarters with a "the rest of you sons-of-bitches got off cheap" ceremony.

The next day it was the shingle splitter from down the road, the oldest of all the loggers, who delivered to her, in a small beautifully hand-carved signed-by-everyone cedar box, a "sympathy egg." She never let on if it was hardboiled.

One logger, not that much later, said he thought he saw her smile. Some weren't so sure about that, but all, with a coffee mug toast, agreed only Gladys could run the show at the Pine Cone Cafe.

On the Ranch Gate

Cowboy, wrangler or buckaroo
Happy to sit and chat with you.

Tourist, guest or "just passin' thru"
Howdy, how do you do?

Cretin, lout, big shot and such
--leave a note; I'll get in touch.

Mountain Ranch Rules. . .

1. Don't criticize the camp cook if you're contrary to cleaning crusty cast iron kettles in a cold creek.

2. Don't count on a spooky horse and a nervous rider to work things out.

3. Don't fault the horse because you fell off.

4. Don't think that "saddlebags" refers to a pair of unattractive cowgirls.

5. Don't blame a horse any longer then he blames you.

6. Don't think all cowboys who make a living in the saddle are numb at both ends.

7. Don't hire a wrangler who believes that his weak reasoning can be strengthened with profanity.

8. Don't think that the trail boss regards "Trying" quite the same as "Doing."

Comes at Once

Spring beams "Good for me"
Grassland meadows edge a big pine tree
Snow still stands on the shady side
Sun slips behind the mountains...hide
And comes at once another season.

Branches embark small needles with sheen
Creek side willows and hay grass gone green
The cows come home to the barbed wire test
Hot days near like a too shy guest
And comes at once another season.

Ice melts, earth's warm and brighter
Moonlight hands clasp a little tighter
Yellow flowers poke up as though escaping hell
While starlings whisper nature's spring bell
And comes at once another season.

The geese talk "geese talk"
And raccoons run the river
Herd-bound fawns and puff-tailed squirrels
Watch smooth beavers slide from
Cottonwoods to boroughs
The coyotes sulk near ever-coveyed quail
Ice skaters leave the Mill Pond
Water returns to reason
And comes at once another summer season.

An Efficient Story

Graeagle isn't just a small town; it's an efficient town.

Efficient to such an extent that apparently the founding father/mother chose to leave the "Y" out of the name. It must have been considered to be in excess of what was sufficient. Even the "Welcome to..." and "Come back again" signs are on the same post. Efficient.

The news is efficient. The weekly newspaper comes out every ten days or so...later, if production is delayed due to news. Which is, sometimes, news of its own. "Flash! Production Delayed!"

You can't dial a wrong number in Graeagle. Why? It's always someone you know and avoiding a conversation now is out of the question. Efficient.

The flashing sign near the school in a nearby town is efficient. It states: "School's Open—Drive CAREFULL." It conveys the need for safety and higher education. The reverse side says: "Go Back!" Efficient.

After the flooded river contaminated another town's water system, the TV news announced: "Boil water for one minute—Cool before drinking." Two health care messages in one. It could also have said:

"Keep your hands off the stove." Would have been a three-fer. Efficient.

"Tree," the tall local tree faller, dropped a tree across his truck. He bucked off both protruding ends and drove the bucked treed truck directly to the bar and parked right in front. No sense having to explain the obvious and no sense having to suffer the raucous verbal thrashing more than once. Efficient.

When your neighbors are not around, use their wood splitter, lawn mower, snow blower, hot tub, bar tab, anything. It's okay! Efficient.

Some tourists don't appreciate the long-standing virtue and tradition of Graeagle efficiency. They tend to conflict with local value by removing the keys from their cars. Inefficient.

Here in the High Sierra, real estate agents downplay to hot-summer home buyers that Graeagle gets snow—Lots of it! This produces spring sellers with "For Sale" signs that pop up like early-thaw wildflowers and a new crop of recycled commissions. Efficient.

Just as an over-zealous real estate marketeer describes a too-small kitchen as "step-saver" so too is Graeagle. Efficient.

In winter, the Public Works Department snowplows roads with such enthusiasm that they always have plenty of summer work: rebuilding trucks, repairing guard rails, and replacing landscaping. Efficient.

The hardware store sells fish bait. They give "For Free" maps with directions to the furthest away "Hidden Hot Spots," thus encouraging purchases of pricey hiking boots and totally useless "Mountain Survival Gear." Efficient.

Business meetings in Graeagle are efficient. They aren't scheduled, agendas aren't outlined, conference rooms aren't booked, minutes aren't taken. Instead they are pick-up-truck, door-to-door, on-the-road encounters. Efficient.

Ben, tired of having most of his thoughts provoke a "How odd..." stare, simply took a big felt marker to his baseball hat: "Warning—I see things differently!" That went well. Efficient.

The only thing in this little town that never fails to work is shared, treasured, and transferred from place to place as needed. It's the all-too-often-appearing sign stating: "Sorry—Out of Order." Efficient.

Chief Graeagle says, "Before you criticize a man, walk a mile in his moccasins." He doesn't say, "then, when you do, you're a mile away and you've got his moccasins." Efficient.

Frank, a local contractor had "Had It" with his ex-employee who started a competing business and then ran to all the jobs Frank was bidding to ask the dollar amount so he could then offer a lower bid. So Frank set a trap by conspiring with one homeowner to bid one job so low that it would cause financial ruin. It did. Efficient.

Billy "the Hill William" had given up using conventional bug spray when, in the middle of one night, he accidentally confused it with nasal decongestant. This spring the warm weather attracted to Billy a new flock of outrageous bugs and unruly women so he invented a "2-in-1" detractant when he tied a urinal cake to the back of his John Deere baseball hat. He called it a "bug and chick anti-magnet." Efficient.

Brandon, a master of fine print, was absolutely certain that the winner of the "Liars Dice Game" had cheated. Opposed, though obliged to write out a check for $100, he evened the score by noting on the memo line for the bright-eyed bank teller to discover when the check was presented "THIS IS A HOLD-UP!" Efficient.

Irish Gerry the concertina player in a folk band called "Whiskey Dents" offered no explanation for his mangled pickup truck. Efficient.

Clem named his new little pup "Enterprise." He knew that a pup doubles as a chick attractant and he needed all the help available. He decided to lend it out to other needy Clem-like bachelors. The pup suffered a bad rap when word got out that the motto for

Enterprise the rental pup was "We'll pick you up." One savvy woman saw through the ploy, snatched up Enterprise, and is now the new owner. She is trying to turn that dog into a man killer. Efficient.

She looked lovingly into her new boyfriend's eyes and requested that he select "their" song. Feeling the effects of "Stage One Commitment," he jumped on the topic and without hesitation offered up the romantic ballad by Andrea Bocelli "Con Te Partiro." He failed to mention the English translation: "Time to Say Goodbye." Efficient.

At the local bar known as the "So-So Corral," it appeared that the next set of angry, attacking words would start a fight between a vacationer and the local "Hick." After the vacationer made a disparaging reference about the Hick's mother, the response came in a rather dramatic Shakespearean tone. The Hick, notwithstanding the slight misquote, stated: "Would that it were there were two of you, for one, harboring such contempt and disdain, would surely dispatch of the other."

The vacationer countered with a bewildered "Huh?"—and his untimely quizzical pause opened the door for a massive right hook. The immediately unconscious "new student of literature" skidded to a halt under the pool table just as the jukebox belted out "—And they call the thing a rodeo." The one-two punch game was over. Efficient.

One out-of-work instructor taught a pricey seminar on negotiating skills. It was such a lousy course that all attendees requested a full refund. After listing the many reasons why the lesson was a failure, they soon learned that their proposed settlement offer was rejected. The instructor refused their demand insisting that they had no negotiating skills. Efficient.

The casinos in Reno are 50 miles away. Gasoline there sells for ten cents a gallon less. Some townspeople claim that they drive to Reno to buy their gas. Efficient.

Crew-Cut ran the local gas station and he was in charge of maintenance of the volunteer fire department's only truck. His house caught fire late one night. Crew-Cut and all the other volunteers raced to the truck and were alarmed when it failed to start. The old corroded battery had sparked its last. They all gave a smoldering glare to Crew-Cut and with combined effort and bravado, pushed the truck out of the shed and swapped into it the new battery from Crew-Cut's car. Efficient.

In this county, the drunk driving laws are enforced, although strangely enough, all bars have parking lots. Every day someone has to leave a truck parked all day at the bar for the sheriff to keep an eye on —their "designated decoy." Efficient.

When he pulled up to the bar, one able-bodied man knowing that he was going to stay for quite awhile and consume until he was impaired, gave an obvious pre-emptive notice by parking in the handicapped spot. Efficient.

In the morning the single gentleman left a note for her to find: "Bet you thought I'd say I love you. Bye." Efficient.

Adhering to the practice of "truth in advertising" and "getting directly to the point," two Graeagle carpenters, Able and Notso, formed a company called "Low Bidders Construction." Their motto was "We promise to do it wrong for less." They did. Efficient.

The gal who operates the local bookkeeping service has a calculated, intuitive sense of cash flow and profit and loss. She's so good that when one of her clients shows up for an appointment she knows, without a glance, if he brought his checkbook. Efficient.

The short, round, over-made-up, over-jeweled-up and more-than-sufficiently obnoxious tourist lady, apparently bemoaning the price of grapes at the Graeagle Store, patiently snitched and stuffed and ate her way to a bargain. Efficient.

The Graeagle IQ Test: If you can't spot the village idiot in this town, it might be you. Efficient.

The Yard Sale IQ Test: "6 quarters for a dollar." Any Takers? No. Efficient.

When asked, "How are you?" he responded by saying that he was much better since he had given up hope. Efficient.

The way to make a small fortune in this small town is to start with a big one. Efficient.

While digging post holes in soft ground, Bill was thinking ahead to the next job where the ground would be rocky. He decided to take a whole truck load with him. Efficient.

Slim just never got around to looking up the word "procrastination." Efficient.

Don, the head wrangler, guided four-day wilderness pack trips through the mountains from Graeagle to Sierra City. He believed that couples who weren't married had no business sleeping together... and those who should no longer be married had no business being on his pack trips. He decided that a "trail boss" is equivalent to a "ship's captain" and, with high-on-a-mountain pomp and trail-side circumstance, he ceremoniously preached from the "Horse Packer's Bible." Reading with stoic purpose, irreverent, irrelevant passages about how to rig a "diamond hitch" and how to read the "logs, ducks and blazes" trail markers, he married two unsuspecting couples with woven rusty baling wire rings. With absolute finality he divorced three grateful couples who, with wild abandon, flung their no-longer-valued wedding rings far into Little Bear Lake. Efficient.

“Busted,” so named for having foolishly attempted to break too many horses, generously helped the town go hi-tech, and he also helped himself. He modified the community bulletin board by adding an around-the-corner extension cord that went to nowhere and a big “Send” button. Across the top he stapled a fancy new sign: “The Facts Machine. Put fifty-cents in the box, point and click.” Efficient.

She was hopeful that the attractive stranger would introduce himself. He finally walked over, extended his hand and said: “Goodbye.” The reality could never be as fascinating as the illusion. Efficient.

Some people, who we wished lived in some other town, don’t bounce back from the bottom. They hit it hard, choose to stay and cling to it like a new home, a safe place from which to shift the burden to others for their self-inflicted demise. Efficient.

Attempting to reduce language to a manageable inventory, one 80 proof connoisseur explained one evening that if two words define each other in the dictionary, then they are to be considered self-canceling and therefore neither exists. Efficient.

He wanted to meet the new gal in town and started the conversation by saying: “Tell me all the things about you that you’d rather I not know.” Efficient.

A perspective employee noted at the top of her job application form that she had recently relocated to these Northern "SEARA" Nevada Mountains. Her not-going-to-be employer silently complimented her for inadvertently demonstrating how she had saved him additional time and effort as he tossed the not-read-any-further synopsis into the trash. Efficient.

Single people have it pretty easy in Graeagle. There is always a new, interesting, personable opposite connection to be found behind every palm tree. Efficient.

He couldn't quite read the roadside sign, so he stopped his truck long enough to let the windshield wipers catch up with the snow. The sign said "Watch for Snow." Efficient.

During a cold morning stop for coffee, he had just started to tell the attractive waitress that the "headlights are on..." when he noticed that she, with an involuntary reflex action, folded her arms and obtrusively raised them up attempting to cover her massive breasts, "on the white Ford pick-up outside" he quickly added. His counter-mate, pretending not to notice, giggled his way to his truck and turned off the lights. Both embarrassment and a battery were spared. Efficient.

One local bartender was asked by some of his patrons, after he had once again demonstrated his unquenched propensity for absurdity and a well-honed lack of chivalry, if he wouldn't be more comfortable sitting outside on the porch with his nose against the wall. He obligingly displayed good judgment when he complied. Efficient.

At the dump you pay only $5.00 to drop off a dead car battery. At the dump you can buy a car battery that needs charging for $10.00. Efficient.

While explaining his contempt for those whose imaginations limit them to speak in platitudes and clichés, he inadvertently demonstrated a self-inflicted contradiction when he described his reaction as akin to "fingernails on a blackboard." Efficient.

Soon after his return flight landed, he realized she had apparently been "too busy" to pick him up at the airport. He negotiated with the cab driver to accept, in exchange for the $80 fare, all of her possessions. Once home, everything from her closet was quickly crumpled into the trunk of the dead-headed-out-of-town taxi. Efficient.

In an attempt to disprove the notion that, in a town like this, there may not be much to see but what you hear makes up for it, Dean started an all-too-free enterprise called "Guided Peeping Tom Tours." He painted his clients with face camo and rented out star-light scopes and bullet-proof vests. They weren't much to see but what you heard made up for it. Dean wasn't much to see but what he heard made up for it. Efficient.

The cowboy emptied the water trough at the horse barn and refilled it with plenty of Budweiser and ice. At the bar he nailed up a sign: "Free Beer at the Barn! — 4 p.m." A lot of beer wranglers showed up to take advantage. At 4:30 the truck and trailer arrived with 40 tons of alfalfa. Efficient.

. . . Six months later the cowboy did it again. As he learned who his friends were, they learned that this time there was no truck, and the massive steaks hit the barbecue. Efficient.

To discourage "locals" from being so upset that they would consider some kind of revenge for having been obviously, personally, and sometimes viciously, characterized in these stories, they were all threatened with the potential of having additional tales printed that were currently, temporarily, tabled. A limited supply of Secret De-coder Rings is still available. Efficient.

...More Mountain Ranch Rules...

9. Don't think that a pricey horse and a fancy saddle make for a better horseman.

10. Don't wonder why a horse might be "Trailer Shy" if you haven't ridden in one.

11. Don't think that, since a good horse and a bad one eat the same amount, you shouldn't look a gift horse in the mouth.

12. Don't believe everything you think.

13. Don't trust anyone who says, "I'd never do anything to hurt you."

14. Don't attempt to "Winter-Out" with her if you haven't figured out her subtle messages.

15. Don't think gossip doesn't ride a fast horse.

16. Don't hurry a pack-horse if you haven't got time to pick up the scattered gear.

Main Event

Angels fought the devil
To a stand off of a war
The devil kicked and bit
The angels punched and swore
Judges pondered
Kept notes and score,
The topic not resolved
The issue holds the floor.

Just what are the things
Good men go to hell for?

I.C.O.Y.

Again, this spring, the two old men talked and laughed together as they shared youthful stories almost in tempo to the swing songs of the '40s playing on the radio.

During these occasional episodes of "who remembers a distant and nearly forgotten story," the long-winded event seemed never complete without one or the other starting again to tell, as if new, the one about "the discovery."

As *Sentimental Journey* hummed in the background, they retold the story to each other, alternating lines as if they had been scripted.

Many years ago, as just kids, they had spent an afternoon tossing rocks into a not-too-deep pool formed by the creek creeping over huge, creviced boulders.

As rock after rock was gleefully flung, yet failed to enter orbit, each remaining hollow cradle in the sandy ground was ceremoniously leveled smooth by the tip of a soggy canvas shoe. The reason for this honor-bound ritual, their first team invention, was known but to these two creek mates. Perhaps that simple act, only that, was the foundation for a life-long bond.

After yet another mighty rock had been launched, the rotation of the wet, dirty shoe in perfect arc to perform a one-swing backfill was stopped short of completion when the operator noticed that the now-missing rock had left exposed a tiny black jewelry box, not shiny, not new, but weary and unused to the bright sunlight. The discovery and its ensuing anticipation of unknown treasure halted the frolic and banter. The creek suddenly seemed louder.

And as this old story was retold, the still evening air filled with the introduction to *Moonlight in Vermont.*

Ever so gingerly, with shared sacred wonder, the young team had knelt, held, and opened the fragile little box.

The sun ricocheted off the bright gold necklace. The heart-shaped locket on the chain appeared like a smaller sun blazing back from the wrong direction. The intense light caused, in each of the boys, a momentary soundlessness. Only momentary, as a slowly unisoned "Oh, Wow!" inadvertently came forth apparently to test the truthfulness of the find.

The amazing yet confusing discovery became even more so when the fine engraving encased within the locket came into focus. The simple message seemed to form a complex code. Nothing more, nothing less; just the initials I.C.O.Y.

The radio thumped out *Moonlight Serenade.*

The two young finders of the hidden treasure discussed, during the nervous hike back to the small country town, their new quarry and their new quandary. At issue was whether to begin asking townspeople if any knew what the necklace was doing there, and just what the initials I.C.O.Y. stood for. This would inevitably tip off the discovery of their secret good fortune. Someone, they feared, employing fact or fancy, would surely lay claim to ownership and rights to title would have to transfer.

Keeping the necklace, by keeping the secret, seemed to be a great idea. But the resulting absolutely-no-chance-of-ever-breaking-the-code penalty seemed to add to the free-for-nothing price they had paid, and would continue to pay.

They were curious about the initials and just as curious as to why one without the other, the necklace without the code or the code without the necklace, seemed less than a bargain. It was a knowledge or possession paradox: a tradeoff.

Over the years, it had become evident that neither could ever recall one or the other having made a conscious choice. The necklace was safe and treasured and shared only between them. They had paid for it by surrendering their almost overwhelming curious desire to decipher the secret, perplexing message.

One old rumor, maybe even a legend, had occasionally circulated among the older townspeople usually around Memorial Day. It had tantalizingly offered the only clue to the history and meaning of the necklace.

Some spoke of a tall, handsome young army Private who, just before he was to ship out to the European Theater during World War II, had planned a picnic at the creek with the gal he was courting.

Something so inconsequential would have otherwise not been noted or recalled, except this was different. For some reason, his long careful planning and contagious excitement in anticipation of his waterside date with his best gal seemed to affect all he encountered. Perhaps those who noticed his enthusiasm, confounded by his otherwise shy nature, secretly cheered him on. He could not, and perhaps did not even try to conceal his affection for the girl next door.

It might have been that this memory was still strong because the townspeople could recollect how they had each felt just a little better about all things during those three days as they watched him make all the secret arrangements for what would surely be love's first step.

Maybe he would confess his adoration, maybe she would promise to write. Maybe he would admit that he was scared of the war, and maybe she would say that she would wait for him.

Some had heard that the Private had advanced through France, through Belgium and into Germany and that he had also advanced through Private First Class through Corporal and into Buck Sergeant. But no one ever heard more about him. He never came home.

Of course only the young boys knew of the necklace found many years later, and only they imagined just how the Private and the necklace might have been connected. They envisioned that the Private had planted, under the rock, the beautiful golden surprise to be presented at just the right moment; assuming, of course, that all went well.

They wondered if she had been receptive to his devotion. They contemplated if a previously unspoken fondness for him had grown within her. They speculated as to if it had been the right time for him to acknowledge and disclose his affection. Had his message been clear and strong? How had it been received?

They considered the character of the man who challenged the uncharted waters that lay ahead of him in all directions.

Sometime after the war had ended, few took note that the quiet young lady had moved away.

The two old creek buddies listened to the radio and with the usual split-second synchronized precision together correctly identified the next tune as *And the Angels Sing.*

Maybe her reaction had made his secret gift inappropriate. Maybe he had changed his mind, or maybe he had sensed that she could not appreciate the strength of his conviction behind the definition of the initials. Maybe she had not shown up. Maybe he had eaten the picnic-for-two, tossed the flowers into the flowing creek and had left the necklace and his feelings under the rock.

But what had he wanted to say? What was the message, the code, the secret he might have hoped they could share?

That part had never been revealed.

Love's locket held secure.

The two old friends finished this discussion, this retelling to each other, with the same question that they had shared for so many years: Just what did I.C.O.Y. mean? Resignation had found a tiny handhold. The Private's secret was very safe with them. They both knew that their mystery-in-common had become, for them, a wonderful gift.

The next song on the radio seemed to call an end to the Memorial Day discussion. And again, the evening ended like all the others; with no discovery—no revelation.

The radio played on and this time both old men were stumped as to the title of the song. It was shortly after the men had left the porch to retire that the quiet voice of the radio announcer concluded the evening's broadcast by saying: "Friends, from 1941, the name of that song was *I Concentrate On You*. . . Goodnight."

...More Mountain Ranch Rules...

17. Don't believe that the Cattle Boss thinks highly of you if he says that you're smarter than a post hole.

18. Don't think your words are near worth your actions.

19. Don't pee in someone else's pool of tranquility.

20. Don't think that the luck of Orion over your shoulder replaces common sense.

21. Don't think that getting what you wanted would have been any better than the experience you got.

22. Don't lean off the side of a horse to open another man's gate if you're not sure which way the owner's attitude swings.

23. Don't grab the branding iron from the fire if you're not sure how far "hot-up-the-handle" it is.

24. Don't think that horses named "Hell Bitch" and "Sweetheart" haven't got a lot in common.

Memorial Weekend, 1988

Snow covered the 1st of June
Horses shivered spring's cold tune
Winter came but twice that year
As nature's clock slipped out of gear.

First-cut alfalfa got caught on the ground
Spring calves froze within Momma's sound
The elements and odds seemed to conspire
As ice wind broke the stretched barbed wire.

The Cowboy fought to accept and call it funny
But knew the weather spent the last of his money
To give and work and hope and try
Beyond tears, son-of-a-bitch—cowboy's cry.

Birth of a Salesman

Great marketing is fun to watch.

Used car salesmen, used-up politicians and multi-use vegomatic hucksters all pitch their wares with a common theme—"Lookie, lookie, look right up here, folks, a visual wonder, I'm sure you'll all agree, it's a veritable rarity and modern marvel of the universe that will not only ease life's burdens, but make life itself worth living! Yesiree, watch closely now..." as the new and improved is presented with carnival style sideshow and hype constructed with equal parts drama and "conviction." Selling has become an enthusiastic attempt to make believable of the totally absurd, and a necessity of the totally useless.

Put your money where your want is.

Happiness is just a payment away.

Come on, friends...let some salesman have his day in the sun.

<u>The Problem:</u>

As we all know, the truly useful things hit the marketplace a long time ago. Wheelbarrows and pie cupboards, good leather boots and rubber bands — tough to improve upon.

Newness with any value is more difficult today, and therein lies an irreparable calamity. Inventors, designers and creators have to appease salesmen begging for the latest "innovation," and must attempt to develop something else we don't need. The poor souls have become yoke mates of despair and lament. More useless products aren't needed, but a greater market share will always be.

Salesmen don't die.

A Solution:

Product developers need simply to create an additional purpose for an already useful device. For example, a secondary function of salt is to melt ice off the walkway.

Baking soda is used to freshen refrigerators, and Coca Cola cleans the crud off car batteries. Even food fights have given brussel sprout farmers cause to rejoice.

Today's marketeers need only to develop an alternate use for an existing item to claim increased product demand, therefore sales, therefore fame, therefore fortune.

A Proposal:

The lowly toilet paper has an untapped potential for an alternate use — more than the current, but limited, practice of cleaning eyeglasses, starting campfires, or the occasional stuffing of some all-too-hopeful prom night brassiere. Even more than the use by Halloween hooligans who create ghost teepees in the trees in front of your home, this new alternate use plan could cause sales of toilet paper to double ply.

The little known truth is that toilet paper can be a very effective hunting tool. The technique, as experienced woodsmen know, is simple. Deer—both white tail and mule—can be caught with toilet paper.

Let Me Explain:

Just as a rabbit will run down the road trapped between the boundaries of a truck's headlight beams, deer can be ushered into a toilet paper corral that is strung among the pines, and they will not attempt to break through or jump over the formidable white-line barrier.

Here's How:

A four-foot high stripe of TP creating a room-sized holding pen is ribboned around a nice stand of conifers with, of course, a gate left open. Deer are then enticed into the corral by employing either of two methods. The most commonly used is to sneak behind the unsuspecting deer and drive them cattle style into the waiting corral. "Get along little doe-y" seems to be the lyric of choice. The second method is to simply wait motionless inside the corral and sound like salt lick. This takes practice, but has been met with measurable, albeit limited, success. Once the pen is occupied, the trap is sprung by simply installing the gate—a closing band of TP strung across the opening.

TP, you know, stands for "temporary pen."

The deer is now yours and can be quickly dispatched with a shovel—uh, a secondary use for shovels.

You may have unwittingly noticed hunters prepared to employ this technique. A telltale indicator is that they will pack into the jeep both the toilet paper and the shovel within close proximity to each other.

But Back to Marketing:

It's easy to envision the toilet paper manufacturers and their duty-bound sales staff leaping at the chance to create television advertisements. A Marlin Perkins-type holding a roll and shovel while expounding on the theme "When Nature Calls," or perhaps a testimonial by Clint Eastwood, "Go ahead, make my Charmin."

Now don't be too quick to "pooh-pooh" these concepts.

Sales enriching contests could be centered around the question of which is more effective; Two ply? Prints? Quilts?

The Benefits:

As with most creative endeavors, there would be some positive spin-off results.

The National Rifle Association might at first be offended, but they'll realize that hunter safety has universal appeal, and we all know that toilet paper doesn't go off accidentally.

The NRA would enjoy substantial dollar savings by not having to combat legislative attempts to regulate the use and control of toilet paper.

The new NRA battle cry might be, "Defend all citizens' rights to arm themselves with toilet paper." Revenue-producing hats and emblems would be emblazoned with the toilet paper and shovel logo. NRA-approved toilet paper holsters would be in demand, and pricey bumper stickers would abound proclaiming, "Hell no, I won't register my roll."

The Conclusion:

I offer this marketing coup without reservation or restraint to the toilet paper manufacturing conglomerates of the world, royalties can be sent c/o Horse Feathers Inc.

...More Mountain Ranch Rules...

25. Don't rummage through the camp first aid kit if the only thing busted is your attitude.

26. Don't believe that *punchin' doggies* is anything at all like what it sounds.

27. Don't let another wrangler's B.S. bother you unless you're not good at giving it back.

28. Don't think conflicts between your head and your heart can't be settled by putting your butt in a saddle.

29. Don't think the best solution for a horse isn't sometimes high speed lead poisoning.

30. Don't think there isn't a whole lot more to being a cowboy than just wearing boots.

31. Don't toss feed hay into the oncoming wind.

32. Don't wash your mud boots off in the water trough.

Love and Seasons

Love and seasons flow together
Like wine
One explodes in a day
The other takes time
One stays—lasts awhile
The other leaves with a faded smile
One in contrast to the past
The other proves hope true at last
And one from the other I should untwine
With heart or soul or body or mind
But a song together they seem to sing
Come on now—hurry home spring.

Thou Shalt Not Pray

Uncle Ernie doesn't live in snow country any more. He grew up in Iowa, and it was a carefully thought-out decision never to live anywhere near snow again.

That should be the end of the story, but no — Uncle Ernie can't leave it at that. He has to joke and tease and belittle those of us who live in Graeagle. He is convinced we aren't nearly as wise as he is.

He smirks from the California coast when we get slammed with a winter snowstorm. He mocks and ridicules our apparent foolishness as we bundle up, chain up, lock hubs, shovel out, and cuss at snow blowers. He gloats about his good sense and our lack thereof. He cheers weather reports that threaten "mountain snow." He laughs at our "who's going to tow the other back onto the road" headaches. From afar he takes great joy in believing that he contributes to the source of the comedy because he "Prays for Snow."

At the start of every snow season, Uncle Ernie always sends some token of what he considers to be his clear thinking and our poor judgment. One year it was a little pink toy beach shovel — plastic, of course. Another time it was a silly home-made "two-man shovel" — a second handle had been installed where the scoop should have been.

But when the newest shovel arrived, it caused a snow war. The latest "cute" shovel had a pretty black bow tied to the handle. Painted on the scoop was, "Do you hear what I hear?" What? Like a tree falling in the forest the non-sound of snow fall? Or just the echo of our cussing and his laughing? No, it apparently referred to the boastful sound of his good reasoning.

The ridiculous new shovel mockingly leaned against the log wall next to the front door of the Lou Ella Mae's Coffee Shop.

The early morning, sloppy boots, cold hands, coffee shop conversation centered around the common theme of, "That's enough of this damn snow!"

It was agreed by all that, once again, the snowstorm was brought to us courtesy of Uncle Ernie. All had endured enough of his gloating and it was time to make him pay. It was time to teach him not to "Pray for Snow." It was unanimously decided that Uncle Ernie's malice should, at least, cause him to get stuck with the cost of everyone's coffee.

A quickly-scribbled sign-up sheet for "Free Coffee" slammed onto the counter.

Lou Ella Mae fired the first bullet at Uncle Ernie by billing his "Account" for a five-dollar tip. Additional charges seemed to snowball from there as all the boys at the coffee shop signed up and drank up.

When Uncle Ernie called the next day to gleefully report that the weather forecast warned of "More snow in the mountains," he couldn't resist making a smart-ass comment equating the freezing point on a thermometer to the I.Q. of snow country bumpkins.

That did it!

He was told that the bill at the coffee shop for "Praying for Snow" was going to be sent to him.

He begrudgingly said, "Well, O.K., how much can a couple of cups of coffee cost?"

Not too long after that, Uncle Ernie received the following letter regarding his account:

Hello, Uncle Ernie:

Well, thought we better give you a status report on how your "Free Coffee" deal is going. We say, "Pretty Good!"

It has snowed for another twelve days in a row, and every day starts at the coffee shop with a new "sign-up and charge-to Ernie" roster. Seems you may have caused yourself a small problem. Locals now refer to Lou Ella Mae's Coffee Shop as "Ernie's Cafe."

Each morning we all meet at "Ernie's" which now opens earlier to accommodate the usual group and the C.B. informed log-truck drivers who fill up, at your expense, their pricey half-gallon thermoses.

Bert started an "Ernie's Coffee" Delivery Service called "B & E's." His expense account, to be billed to you, includes gas at $3.79 per gallon and four new snow chains.

Word got out to the cattle ranchers and now cowboys, after gathering strays, converge for perhaps the first time in their lives at the cafe they now call "The Bistro." Refills aren't free during long discussions while cowboys settle in with boots up rather than in the stirrups. Graeagle is now on the verge of getting nothing done. Thanks a lot, Ernie.

A lot of guys were asking for coffee and Baileys, I said "sure," didn't think you'd have a problem with that, $6.75 each.

The other coffee shop in town couldn't compete with the "Charge-To-Ernie Giveaway-Program"—so now *they* fill up at "Ernie's," sign the charge account, and follow suit.

Last Sunday the priest from the Catholic Church formed an after-mass field trip with the whole congregation to witness "Ernie's Power of Prayer." Boy, those people can really drink!

Lou Ella Mae is hoping she can keep your cost down to $3.25 per cup but not sure with the extra staff and all.

Oh fine, the town's only mimeograph machine exploded while trying to run off so many copies of the "Free Coffee" sign-up roster. The repair man, working overtime, stapled the bill for parts and labor to your charge account.

Proceeds from the "Ernie Prays for Snow" coffee mugs, retailing for $12.95, are being donated to the local ski-slope operator. You are being billed only $8.95 each (plus tax).

The Mercantile now sells "Ernie's Snow Shovels" and sure wants to talk with you about being a sponsor.

Lou Ella Mae is thinking about charging your account with one of those big, expensive copper and brass espresso machines. She's going to label it with an engraved brass plaque: "Ernie's Boiling Point."

Slim suggested that an additional charge to the account might be wisely invested in a snow making machine for the entrance of the coffee shop so that "Ernie's Deal" can run through August.

And one of the more pricey foam-topped coffee blends frequently requested is called "Shovel This!"

The Folgers coffee distributor is sending you some kind of thank you note. I asked about a volume discount—he said that because it now takes two men to make the massive deliveries—the price went up. Sorry.

As a courtesy to you, Lucille, the coffee shop accountant who is tracking your billing, reduced her hourly rate to $80.

The local newspaper is pretty sure the article about your generosity will print long before the storms stop and is excited about the story being picked up by Associated Press and Greyhound Bus Tours.

A *minor* accident in "Ernie's" parking lot between a county snow plow and seven cars seems to have gotten a bit out of control. Not only did opposing attorneys and insurance company representatives gather to demand your name and address, but the local District Attorney is concerned: "Just who supplied all the coffee and Irish Whiskey…." Ooops!

The police collected copies of the pertinent "Ernie's" sign-up pages. That may not have been a good thing.

My attorney carefully looked into your predicament; his bill to you will be forthcoming. He decided to represent one of the parties that is going to sue you. If it will help, I can send to you half of the referral fee he kicked back to me. He commented on the "Free Coffee" sign-up sheet saying: "Thanks Ernie, see you in court."

The train engineer's unscheduled and unauthorized parking of the westbound freight blocked all traffic into town as he sat at "Ernie's" for two hours. He yelled from the back of the police car something about the legal responsibility of one who creates an "attractive nuisance." Western Pacific will get in touch—uh, that went well.

I told them they better not mess with you! Uh, that didn't go so well...

Clem thought he'd only have to bill you for the shear pins on his new snow blower. It turns out it's the transfer case. The parts supplier said a whole new blower might be cheaper. Your choice.

The 6 tea drinkers in town are a little upset with you. You didn't offer to buy their tea and those sign-carrying protestors started an "Anti-Ernie" petition. They quickly got enough signatures to file a class-action discrimination law suit against you.

Offers from attorneys, far and near, willing to substantially discount their contingency fee for the opportunity to be plaintiff's counsel have swamped the tea party headquarters. Since the local jury pool is tainted, the current thinking is to motion for a change of venue to some other county.

Shoot. That might affect the cost of your defense.

In the case of "The Graeagle Tea Party vs. Uncle Ernie" bookies have you at a 7 to 1 underdog. I billed your account $25 for the bet I placed on you hoping to lower the odds.

Doing what I can to help...that's me all over.

St. Patrick's Day (...and night) at "Ernie's" was a hoot! Lucky for you I managed to get your credit card number.

At the party, the coffee-stained "Uncle Ernie Prays For Snow" tee shirts you bought sold out quickly. All proceeds benefit the jittery caffeine addicted waitress currently in rehab. She was pretty thorough with her sailor-like comments about you as the County Mental Health Department loaded her, in full body restraints, into the ambulance.

This may not be a good time for you to come into town.

Well, now you've got a problem: It seems that Starbucks wants to talk to Lou Ella Mae at "Ernie's" about a franchise agreement for "Ernie's Deal" at all of their "above-the-snowline" shops. Better have your accountant give us a call.

Sweet ol' Harriette at first thought you were being taken advantage of and that one man shouldn't get all the blame for a long winter. As she was leaving the coffee shop she slipped on the ice and fell hard. It was just unfortunate that both EMTs were wearing "Uncle Ernie Prays For Snow" tee shirts. Golly, she sure spends a lot of her recovery time filling out legal reports and forms. Lump Lump thinks it's just fine. Now he has no need to shovel out her house for at least 6 to 8 weeks.

Folks in the down-river towns that are now flooding are turning heavenward and asking just how it could be that the mountains got such an outrageous snow pack this year. Swartz, his truck loaded with sandbags charged to your account, spray painted the plywood side boards on his pick-up with your phone number and the name of your insurance company. Sorry.

You'll be pleased to note his bill to you for the cost of driving to Salt Lake City to pick them up was somewhat offset by the savings he made on the cost of the bags. Swartz, sometimes the dumbest duck on the pond, thought he was doing you a favor by saving money on a great buy of "On-Sale" sand bags. Apparently he didn't foresee the disadvantage of sandbags that "can be loaded from either end."

The boys down at "Ernie's Snowed-In Cafe" started a fundraiser to honor you. Every time one of the iced-up, pissed-off "customers" cusses at Ernie for having caused the non-stop snow, they are required to toss their change into the jar.

The one who is best at it wins the pot.

Jimmy figured that he was already in for about $30.

Wally, a wilderness product of isolation and an otherwise soft-spoken man, gave a full-color, ten-minute, outrageous, rafter-shaking presentation to a band of cheering, stomping, standing-room-only, coffee-drinking, ice-laden snow shovelers. His masterful weaving of all the trophy words ripped and tore at Ernie and earned unfiltered respect and unanimous approval. Wally was awarded and proudly pocketed $147.

Well, got to go now—it's snowing pretty hard and we've got to shovel out the overflow parking lot at "Ernie's." The guys that I hired for you need your Worker's Compensation information and Employer's I.D. number for unemployment benefits.

Looks like another week of snow—we'll keep you posted.

We all say "Thanks, Uncle Ernie!"

Signed:
The Boys at the Coffee Shop

...More Mountain Ranch Rules...

33. Don't fry camp bacon in the nude.

34. Don't scoop poop on a rainy day.

35. Don't fix the fence without knowing what side the bull's on.

36. Don't leave your hay hooks on the wrangler's saddle.

37. Don't wear a belt buckle bigger than a hubcap.

38. Don't wash your backside upstream in the camp creek.

39. Don't get in the bed roll with your spurs on.

40. Don't tie your horse to a tent stake.

The Critics Rave . . .

1. Rarely does a book have such an impact; this one leaves a high velocity mark:
   ---a mark in the wall,
   ---a far flung mark in the truck across the street,
   ---and, mark my words, a mark in the garbage can.

   Lloyd the Neighbor

2. Seldom does an author demonstrate such fine writing skill as "Full Money Back Guarantee." If I could only bill him for the time spent suffering.

   Vance the Horseman

3. Mountain men with his literary style are few and far between, just not few and far enough. He should have considered the trees he could have spared had he the wisdom not to print.

   John Muir

4. The magic of a wordsmith's talent escapes most of us. This author proves that the calamity might be more universal than originally feared and demonstrates just why reading may be on the verge of becoming a lost passion.

   Donna the Cuttin' Wrapper

5. Were this a book of seafaring adventures, I'd say, "Stick with me kid, I know where the lifejackets are."

   Lori

...More Mountain Ranch Rules...

41. Don't drink your whiskey unless you brought enough for all.

42. Don't shoot it, catch it or trap it if you're not gonna eat it.

43. Don't get so mad you want to spit.

44. Don't say "Howdy" if you'd rather say "See ya."

45. Don't think anything else is "just like riding a bicycle."

46. Don't tell a long story if silence puts you in a better light.

47. Don't point the direction if you can't read a compass.

48. Don't think coming in a beat late makes you syncopated.

Road Home

Ease right, tighter right
The mother earth and her sun
One lays the land, the other's on the run
Bends and swirls in comic turns
And all done just for fun
Barb-to-wire and post-to-hole
The cows and the field are one
Snows unlocked
Soon summer's burn
Road tight, narrow sight,
And tighter to the turn.

What Daddy Wants for Christmas

He had always known that those simple conversations he enjoyed with that little six-year-old kid were much more meaningful than the momentary smiles they created and shared.

Her young questions seemed to prompt lighthearted ramblings between the two of them. He was a man with no children of his own and she was a child without a dad, so it hadn't been long, it seemed, until they just adopted each other.

So, too, it appeared that it hadn't much mattered what they were doing together. It always became more interesting when they explored the many possible answers to her many impossible questions.

As he stacked firewood, and she helped as best she could, they pondered how anyone might know if the light really went off when the refrigerator door closed or just how many different colors the sky could be. More than the usual colors of dark blue and slate gray, sunset red and thunderstorm black, but also how in spring the winds could lift the pine pollen and the skies would go green. Or just how in early summer the skies could become white when the breeze would carry the snowflake-type hatch like dandelion fluff off the cottonwood trees, and maybe the dogwood trees would give a pre-emptive shiver thinking nature's clock had slipped out of gear.

They would playfully discuss the difference between "to look and to see," "to listen and to hear," and why, it seems, most rivers run downhill. Or just how it could be that the tall sunflowers know to face the morning sun.

He had always felt that they shouldn't seek out only that which is the "right" answer, but rather the many different answers there could be to any question. She was his hero, and he cheered her on and cherished her being.

Later that winter, sometime between shoveling snow and the obligatory snowball fight, she stopped him cold. He could sense, as her attacking snowballs came less frequently and went well off target, the careful formation of yet another question. She shyly asked, as her eyes looked away, "Daddy, what do you want for Christmas?"

For the first time he didn't know what to say. The question reminded him of her loving, giving nature, but more he felt in his heart his intense love for this little kid. It was the first time she had called him "Daddy."

He realized that this time was going to be different. The answer would have to be more than just a reactive, fun-filled verbal frolic. This question required reflective intensity.

He asked the kid if she would let him write out his answer. She was okay with that and later that evening he gave her this letter:

Dear Kid, What I Want For Christmas:

Nothing with easy-to-follow assembly instructions included, nothing that is the start of a fascinating new hobby, and nothing with anything trendy about it. No ten-day free trial offers, nothing from a book club, record club or chess club. Nothing with the word "collectible," no plates, no coins, and nothing commemorative from a famous mint.

Nothing that is "Loads of Fun," nothing that makes me the life of the party, the envy of all my friends, or lets me be the first on the block. Nothing that can be mastered in twelve easy lessons, is reversible, and nothing that every household should not be without. Nothing that will have to shrink or stretch to fit, nothing that also can be used as a planter, and nothing that chops, slices and dices. Nothing that has many exciting uses "too numerous to mention" and nothing that has to have an explanation attached. Nothing in the newest fashion colors and nothing that every executive should have—and I don't want a tie!

I do want anything you made yourself, anything with your name on it, anything you hammered together with bent nails, anything you built or cut out or pasted up or in any way created. I want anything you thought of, anything your hands and mind tried to do. I want a pretty rock you found, a bird's nest you saved, a story you wrote, a picture you drew, or a song you can sing. I want anything that may have been squished a little on the school bus ride home, or dropped in the dirt, or chewed on by the puppy. It's fine if the wood split, if the paper tore, if the paint ran, if it's not quite flat or square, if it doesn't quite work or if it's otherwise not exactly right. It's even okay if it won't stay beautifully Christmas wrapped. I want anything from your imagination, anything from your world, from your heart, from you.

...and anything from you I will love, like I love you.

...And he signed it, "Daddy."

That was many years ago. Where is she today? If that now-old man were asked he would say that she lives within every kid with a question, within every adult with time to listen and well within every loving Christmas gift.

If you should meet this beautiful young lady, stop and take note, but remember her questions can be tough. She's my kid. I'm her Daddy—always will be.

That year she hand painted a beautiful tin can trimmed with a gold and red ribbon that said: "Daddy, Merry Christm...." She ran out of space for the whole message but saved room for "Love, Kayle."

...and, I love it.

Of course, it has always stood centermost on my desk.

. . .More Mountain Ranch Rules. . .

49. Don't let your horse kiss you on the ass.

50. Don't kiss your horse on the ass.

51. Don't think that ignorance is an art form.

52. Don't start a fire you're not big enough to put out.

53. Don't let your britches ride so tight in the crotch that your brain goes short of blood.

54. Don't round up cattle if you can't read a brand.

55. Don't think a loose cinch isn't a fortune teller.

56. Don't fall a big sugar pine if all you need is kindling.

One Hundred Reasons

Cowboys have that far away look
Caused not by broncs or bulls or horns that hook
But love that came and stayed then went
Good days come and gone and too soon spent
Handheld sunsets when they'd ride and play
With love that visited but stole away.
Another man will have new thoughts and words
Nice times and a plan for all seasons
But will he love you for one hundred reasons?
And if he can, what price he'll pay,
That far away look, now his, will stay
Cowboys come and go that way.

A Bear Bone Story

Both big dogs had always been the best of buddies. Well, not always. The older, taller, yellow one had the advantage of a year or so time in service and time in grade over the smaller brown one, but that had been worked out. Well... not always.

Different attitudes, different appearances and different approaches seemed to contribute to different styles of competitiveness — not an overt hostility, but more of a subtle game of one-upmanship. Who got the preferred bed and who hopped into the pickup first? Who was the first to lead the way down the pine-lined mountain trail and who barked first—if for no other reason than to make the other jump? These issues and others were always considered between the two to be very important.

But the sportsmanship was usually fair and the best buddies could relax together in the sun until some starter's gun, known only to dogs, sounded the next round of showmanship.

Brown Dog, the smaller of the two, had figured out how to carry off both of the proffered bone treats in a single mouthful to a sheltered, selfish retreat — an overt display of "I-win-you-lose" arrogance. It seemed that his climb up the ladder of virtue might have been halted at the first rung.

To the bigger yellow dog, this seemed extremely inconsiderate and would have to be dealt with. The yellow dog reasoned that a patient, carefully-calculated fix would be far more entertaining than a bold confrontation which could also give the other the right to some self-satisfaction.

Although the yellow dog would never have admitted to it, Brown Dog was the more aggressive of the two. He always felt that it was his "better dog" obligation to spend long, extremely exhaustive nights barking and running along the inner safety of the back fence line. He delivered his protective demonstration to the late spring and early summer bears and cubs who came from the woods, and he thought, came way too close, to the ranch house. The following day, an overwhelming conviction to duty left Brown Dog totally committed to nothing more strenuous than passively trying to recover his strength.

Just why the bears came in one, two or three at a time to exactly the same place on the other side of the fence, Brown Dog couldn't figure. But come they did, night after sleepless night, bringing him to all-consuming exhaustion and leaving him to wonder why his antics had, for some strange reason, little or no effect on dissuading the bears from encroaching way too close to his barked-about boundary.

Brown Dog had appointed himself as sentry and always, come daybreak, this bleary-eyed guard resented that the yellow dog slept comfortably with no sense of fear or gratitude. On the other hand, the yellow dog always awoke fresh and alert having enjoyed a great night's sleep on the more favored bed. He was ready for anything. First into the truck, first down the trail, and first to notice that his buddy, Brown Dog, was going to be second at everything all day, he seemed to care not much about the bears—and seemed to wonder even less why they came to the fence line.

Later on, as on all other days, the ritual continued. Brown Dog unfairly, greedily, grabbed both bones, his tail too weary to be held pompously high, and he slowly moved to a place where quiet sleep would be the more highly guarded treasure.

Soon Brown Dog, before he had even sampled the big juicy treasures, was deep in overwhelming sleep. Quietly noticing when this moment arrived, the wise, yellow dog casually recovered the two meaty rewards. He would in a short time enjoy one himself, but first and much more importantly with a diplomat's sense of evenhanded justice, he would march with well-thought-out ceremony to the regular well-established place just outside the fence line. Once there, he would carefully leave one meaty trophy where he knew the bears' fine sense of smell would rake in the scent of the savory feast, causing a great commotion in the night.

The yellow dog geared up for the night-long festivities by selecting for himself again the more preferred bed. That evening he hunkered down early knowing that for Brown Dog it was going to be a full moonlit, long, noisy, exhausting night.

. . . More Mountain Ranch Rules . . .

57. Don't hang your hat on a loose rack.

58. Don't ride up a hill you can't ride down.

59. Don't think time has anything to do with healing wounds.

60. Don't pack your saddle bags with stuff somebody else thinks you need.

61. Don't toss your canteen just 'cause it's empty.

62. Don't hop on your horse if you haven't got a grip on the reins.

63. Don't think there's only one campsite around the lake.

64. Don't pout about getting wet if you thought that the horse you're riding and the pack horse you're leading would jump the creek at the same time.

The Stand Off

A distant young ranch hand began to yell,
"Hey, Cowboy! Come closer, I've something to tell."

Why should I walk so far when I'm so near?
With cupped hands he shouted back,
"Bring what you say — I'll be right here."

Each held position, convinced the other would yield,
And forced a fight from far afield.

But he who moved to make the first blow
Would give the other the right to know
— It was he who came to me.

The Drummer's Song

The Ophir State Prison Marching Band showed up in gray and white striped flannels for the 4th of July parade. It was a small town parade with balloon-toting kids on bicycles who pondered at the "Skunk Cabbage Queen" perched gloriously, yet precariously, atop a Nash Rambler, as she cautiously readjusted her green and yellow crown.

No sidewalks in this little town, just edge-of-the-road fans, cheering on the preschool kids dressed as Smokey the Cubs. And of course, saluting the finest platoon of flag bearing soon-to-be out of step military could-have-beens who stared passionately straight ahead as if silver stars were being awarded just around the bend.

Yep, this was going to be a parade.

Two antique cars gave their sputtered best, but stalled at the start. Soon one began graciously pushing the other with a "show must go on" conviction. The local volunteer fire department towed out their only fire truck. It was the same one that last year after an emergency dispatch, raced back to the fire station with full lights and sirens to get "go the other way" directions.

The fully decorated faded red and gold fire truck finally fired up with a thunderous flaming burst that could have started a fire. The roar of the over-primed explosion did cause the fearless combative kids from the karate school to jump toward each other's open arms as if all were forgiven.

Yep, this was going to be a good parade.

Some smiling vote-seeking politician nobody knew, his meaningless waves greeted with indifference, followed the horses that pooped out the route to victory like well-marked steaming bread crumbs.

And the Ophir State Prison Marching Band did a four-bar-per-beer rehearsal.

In the hot sun the "Ladies of Flower Arranging" took up their soon-to-wilt positions behind the logging company's "Youth with Chainsaws" float.

The very young loggers, balanced on top of the flat bed trailer, fired up in unison their oversized chainsaws with a "mine's bigger than yours" mindset.

Lofting, choking, blue smoke billowed to fill their overhead banner like a sail. Just what that sign referred to as "America's Renewable Resource," whether it was kids, air or trees, was a clear cut of confusion.

And the juggling unicycle rider with a scary clown's face and a soon-to-be-reckoned-with flat tire suddenly seemed very much in place.

Yep, this was going to be a fine parade.

The cowgirls on horses practiced their waves, and with an exhibitionist's flair, dramatically adjusted their padded breast collars. They rehearsed acting nonchalant as if the whole world was watching and they didn't give a damn. In fact, it wasn't and they did.

The puffed-up, suspicious looking, pint-sized deputy sheriff, wearing an oversized gun belt, shot everyone his best "I'm in control" glare. His threats of citations for jaywalking were universally ignored.

He and his little second hand sedan, with matching "I think I can" persona, joined the parade. Some noticed the "your tax dollars at work" decal on the back of his car and perhaps felt very consoled. Others spotted "to protect and serve" and wondered just who was doing what.

Yep, this was going to be a great parade.

All forty members of the Ophir State Prison Marching Band slowly formed into rank and file, sort of. Trumpets, trombones, and tubas too, a massive flat harp and French horns, fell in behind the double belled euphonium, a most disorganized group. Saxophones stood where drummers should be, some facing the wrong direction, a disorder beyond reason.

Some wore comical hats made of paper, or laced-together beer cans, others cowboy hats or firemen's helmets.

One had a rubber chicken strung three feet behind his left ankle and another proudly sported, on his rump, a "Friends don't let Friends drive Fords" bumper sticker.

The piccolo player purportedly packed pre-cooled Pabst Blue Ribbon beer. One band member, wearing an FBI hat, whose fake prison number on his shirt matched the license plate number of the local District Attorney, ceremoniously blew legal bubbles out his kazoo. The bassoon section, judiciously representing the grand jury, obligingly followed without bursting one of his bubbles. They pretended not even to notice and, less of a challenge, not even to care.

The drum major, perhaps the shortest of this over-the-top group, proudly brandished a too large whistle, tall top hat, short long coat tails, and a toilet bowl plunger for a baton.

It was curious just how many spectators might have figured out that there really is no Ophir State Prison, and even, if there was, it may not have had a traveling marching band. It's just that these musicians enjoyed a humorous combination that might baffle some. Their point was simply that humor must be relevant and what's more relevant than to laugh at our own expectations of how serious a marching band should be.

The parade continued and the band played loudly. The theme from the Mickey Mouse Club rattled against the counter melody of "*This Bud's For You.*" But, oh my, those boys could play!

They couldn't march, they couldn't care less, but damn, they could play. First big band, then classical, pop, and Caribbean, the smiling, teasing "prisoners" could play.

Yep, this was going to be a magnificent parade.

In other small towns, they had played out this folly, sometimes marching the parade route head-on from the opposite direction, or diverting off the path into and through a drug store and returning by way of the dress shop.

Once, after taking over the sidewalks and herding the spectators onto the street, corralling them, they played "*Don't Fence Me In.*"

Parades shouldn't be taken so seriously they thought, but they took their music seriously. The most perfect version of Glenn Miller's "*American Patrol*" was followed by the thunder of Benny Goodman's "*Sing, Sing, Sing.*"

So with seemingly irreverent commotion, the band numbers randomly sauntered and crashed into each other, not so much down the route but rather first to the right then to the left. It appeared that not one knew one from the other.

The overrated value of being in step left them bewildered until some careless spectator opened and offered up a large cooler of beer. Quick step mess-hall-type compliance seemed to come from nowhere. The charge fell short of honor when the concept of passing beer from the front to the back seemed out of the question.

The Ophir State Prison Marching Band cared nothing about the fans and even less about their band mates—or so they pretended.

As this magnificent parade lit up the tiny red, white and blue bedecked town, it was a drummer who spotted her standing along the parade route, seemingly alone in a crowd, as plain and as lovely as he had ever seen. He was overcome by her powerful shy elegance, simple understated beauty, a kind, heart-clearing soul. Her demeanor conveyed a subtle honorable nature.

He couldn't call it quits at a glance any more than he could have halted his stare. He didn't smile and she didn't turn her eyes away; it was just an "Oh my God" connection.

The spectators erupted into laughter at the band's ridiculous attempt to "march" to a waltz. Because of her, the drummer lost focus and fought to keep his sticks from fumbling to the ground.

The secret code of the drum major's three whistle blasts followed by four toilet-plunger pumps into the air signaled that the next song would be *"'Til There was You"* from *The Music Man.*

The band played and joked and marched on except for the drummer. As if pulled to a siren's song, he drummed himself out of the corps. Still keeping perfect beat for his marching-away band buddies, he walked over and stood almost without expression in front of this glorious magical lady.

Sometimes an emotional embrace can be so strong that it's just better to let the music go on without you and all sounds drift away.

It was the other drummers in the band who were the first to notice that one of their own was unaccounted for. One at a time each broke rank and joined the passionate drummer's serenade. He played only for her.

The rest of the band continued to march away although their whole drum section was now missing in action.

Each drummer, sensing one had fallen and the importance of the moment, held up in a semi-circle, his own individual drum. Large and small from bass to cymbals, triangles to snares, they created for him a monstrously huge set of drums.

Eye contact between the drummer and the lady held firm. All watched as he furiously played out his heart in passionate expression.

Yep, this was an amazing parade.

The drummer's thunderous love song swelled as did the crowd of spectators who moved in quietly around her. All remembered sparks in their own lives, but perhaps none ever quite like this.

He played with an open-hearted honor for what he sensed was her straight-ahead compassion for life and all things worth loving.

The still marching-away band, now minus the entire percussion section, soon ground to a halt and looked back. One row at a time, they returned to reverently form ever expanding arcs around the drummer and the lady.

When the song ended and started to change to another, it wasn't to the whistled code of the drum major but rather the selection was made by the gloriously beautiful tone of a lone trumpet.

Quietly, slowly, strongly with a resonance only mountain air can support, the trumpeter began to play Glenn Miller's "*I Know Why and So Do You.*"

The band joined in solemn magnificent harmony.

Life's parade had taken a momentary repose as true loving and unspoken sharing held a firm grip on the moment.

A small tear of all-knowing gratitude streaked the quiet lady's face. The people who now seemed to suddenly surround her would later say they thought they saw the same on the drummer.

The band slowly moved back to the center of the street pressured by the impatiently following parade entrants, who acted as if there were a checkered flag at the finish line. No one smiled and no one waved and no one said a word as one-by-one they regrouped to march away. Individually each drummer took down his portion of the impromptu "drum set" and rejoined the marching band as they belted out Jimmy Buffet's

"*One Particular Harbor.*" The lone drummer was last to leave. The parade went on.

Yep, this was a magical parade.

Afterwards, the cowboys graciously offered to help the cowgirls get over being saddle sore. The unicycle rider who had saluted from the stretcher while giving his best "I shall return" impersonation later joined the "Ladies of Flower Arranging" who decided that silk and plastic was in their future.

Not that much later, the proud owner of the little Nash Rambler received a traffic citation for driving too slow in a school zone.

Soon after that, a lone burning tree accidentally ignited by some children with a chainsaw, fell squarely on the old fire truck.

It was sometime later when most thought the politician's concession speech, though he fumbled with his microphone and tried to conceal a belch, must have been slurred by emotion.

The local un-newsworthy newspaper avoided mentioning that the little deputy sheriff had been arrested for shoplifting girlie magazines.

Later still, the "Skunk Cabbage Queen," although she had put on a few more pounds, ran unopposed for a second term.

And the sweet lady, well, she holds hands with the drummer.

And nope, they never miss a parade.

. . . More Mountain Ranch Rules . . .

65. Don't believe the fastest horse to the alfalfa always gets enough to eat.

66. Don't think thinkin' it is the same as being it.

67. Don't set up your bed roll down hill from the picket line.

68. Don't wear knee-high mud boots into a thigh-high creek.

69. Don't think the barbed wire doesn't sometimes hold up the post.

70. Don't think a big grin replaces sincerity.

71. Don't think good intentions replace doing what you said you're gonna do.

72. Don't bet a buck you gotta borrow if you're in just a touch over your head.

What is a Cowboy?

Just what is a cowboy?
Between the security of childhood and the responsibility of adulthood,
Is that mysterious group of humanity called cowboys—
Assorted hat sizes, weights, and stages of sobriety
In cities, towns, and in the wilderness,
Bars, jails, or on the road,
And always in debt.

A cowboy is creativity with a deck of cards
Bravery with spurs
Energy on the dance floor
A legend of the Old West with a copy of *Playboy*
And seldom without a case of beer or fifth of whiskey.

He has the slyness of a fox
The spirit of a dreamer
The stories of a sea captain
The aspirations of a Casanova
And when he wants something, it's usually connected with horses.
... or women
Some of his likes are:
Women
Beer
Horses
Whiskey
Broncos
Rodeos
Dances

Women
Chewing tobacco
And the smell of saddle leather
... Women ...

His dislikes are:
Being told to take his hat off
Officers of the law
Answering letters
And horses without cow sense.

No one else can cram into one pocket
A little black book, the photo of his best gal,
A package of Red Man tobacco chew
And what is left of last week's pay.

He likes to spend some of his money on girls,
Some on poker, a lot on beer,
Some on shooting pool,
And the rest on foolishness.

A cowboy is a majestic creature
You can scratch him out of your phone book
...but not out of your heart.

You may want to give up on that bleary-eyed, good-for-nothing, long-way-from-home lover boy, but all your dreams become insignificant when a cowboy knocks on your door looks at you with those bloodshot eyes and says, "Hi Babe!"

The Screen Door Episode

In the middle of a too-hot summer night, a bear stood on the front porch. Enticed by the left-over aroma of Leroy and Norma's evening meal, the bear figured he would just come on in the house and help himself. He growled and threatened to rip and tear through the expensive new wood-framed screen door.

Sleepy Leroy snatched up his crusty John Deere hat, grabbed the semi-rusted rifle from the closet and, in his gray sagging threadbare underwear, charged to the open front door. Norma, in her pink curlers and canvas nighty and what was left of her mud-packed face cream, quickly caught up with him. One cucumber slice had slid to a halt on her cheek like a dislocated monocle. The other clung to her nighty as if she had been awarded a medal near where her breasts had started. In the moonlight she had become a formidable war-painted screen door avenger.

Just as Leroy came face-to-face with the bear and was about to find out if the old rifle could fire, Norma skidded around the corner and delivered the all-too-familiar hard slap to the back of his head. The impact snapped Leroy into wide awake, dislodged his elastic-long-gone boxer shorts, and foretold that an opinion from Norma would quickly be forthcoming.

Norma shouted, "Criminy, don't shoot through the screen door!"

Leroy's shoulders scrunched. One hand gripped the rifle and the other gripped his shorts and a damn-it-woman look gripped his face. He had suffered an outflanking attack from one front and one back. While wishing he could free one hand to rub the throbbing spot on the back of his head, he decided against asking, "Are you nuts?" Instead, he lowered the gun, and turned toward the scary face and calmly uttered, through tight lips, "Okay, why don't you open it?"

Still having no unoccupied hand to protect himself from what he knew would be an even more thunderous second bop on the head if he were unable to stifle a laugh, he attempted to disguise it as a cough and a hiccup.

Leroy thought that Norma should consider showing less concern for the screen door and more for the back of his head. Her perplexed look shifted to anger at his lack of concern for her well-being, and that didn't go well with Norma.

Leroy had spent more than a considerable amount of time in a life filled with songs of quiet desperation. He now questioned if his life wouldn't be less painful and more reasonable were he with the bear on the other side of the screen door. At least out there motives were clear and threats came at you head on.

The bear's growl, Norma's slap, and his free-falling underwear all whittled away at and threatened to expose his quickly-becoming-belittled manliness. He avoided suggesting to Norma that perhaps she should just step outside onto the porch with the bear and shoo it away with a broom. He reasoned to himself that since the bear wasn't wearing underwear, and could defend himself with two paws, it might be a fair fight.

As Norma contemplated her predicament, it seemed to the bear that other screen doors had never been such a problem. This attempt was as unrewarding as trick-or-treating at a house that passed out celery sticks. The bear, watching the fight escalate, inadvertently rubbed his shoulder against the doorbell. The sound startled Norma who momentarily wondered who would have come calling at this hour of the night. When she figured it out, the ringing bell apparently signaled the start of round two.

The commotion caused the bear some befuddlement. Not wanting to be caught between the two of them, he decided to slowly, cautiously, almost apologetically, back away from the porch.

Both the bear and the screen door survived unscathed.

Leroy was instructed to cuddle with his rifle on the sofa for the rest of the night. He concealed his gratitude and accepted her demand with a mock hint of disappointment.

...More Mountain Ranch Rules...

73. Don't believe the snow always stands longer on the shady side.

74. Don't think the bear always hibernates in winter.

75. Don't think the beaver always dams slow movin' waters.

76. Don't think the field mouse doesn't sometimes nip the coyote.

77. Don't think the eagle doesn't sometimes flap himself in the nuts.

78. Don't think it takes that long for the cows to come home.

79. Don't think a runaway horse knows where he's going.

80. Don't think all trails end up somewhere special.

... And the Critics Rave ...

6. Raw emotion, literary talent and a persuasive point of view are all missing from this "Grab-You-By-The-Pocketbook" rambling absurdity.

   Harston Construction Company

7. Though I do not understand your book, the part about the boobs was really cool!

   Johnny, 4th Grade

8. Best pork chops and sour dough since leaving St. Louis! (Oh, sorry. . . thought you were asking about the Cafe.)

   Slim

9. Momma said if you can't say something nice then you better really mean it, and I mean it!

   The Innkeeper at the Oedipus Complex

10. Writing, to be considered truly exceptional, must be gauged against a low-water bench mark. This might be it. Even the rejection letters from potential publishers were poorly written.

    The Plumas County Literary Guild

...More Mountain Ranch Rules...

81. Don't hesitate to hold your ground in a battle of wits.

82. Don't give yourself more than half-credit for having out-smarted a half-wit.

83. Don't get back on the horse until you've figured out what you did wrong.

84. Don't believe your attitude isn't just a decision.

85. Don't think everyone is entitled to your opinion.

86. Don't light the kindling until you've packed in the firewood.

87. Don't tie your horse to a hitchin' rail you're not willing to fix.

88. Don't fidget with the hay hooks if you're not going to buck the bales.

First Rodeo

Bronco
Big horse
Tight girth
One strong hand on the rawhide
Ahh...what the hell, you'll give it try
Eight seconds ain't that long of a ride
Stetson on as tight as your stomach
Rodeo announcer sings your name
With considerably less roar than your heartbeat
Something's wrong, you thought this was just a
game—

Time stops — nothing is certain —
And why does a chute man smile?
Now don't you wish your mom had never bought
That damn watch with John Wayne on the dial?
Too late, slight nod to the gate —
And the whole crazy world explodes!

The Night Wrangler

Just at sunset, the three horsemen, on a six-day ride from Graeagle to the winter pastures in Grass Valley, rounded the forested edge of Little Grouse Lake and began to set up camp. The saddle and pack horses jostled for position on the picket line as the campfire sputtered to life. The one-back-hoof-slightly-cocked, early-indicator of a horse settling in for the night was interrupted by the limb-busting chaos of a massive bear on the other side of the lake. It had little effect on the horses and even less on two of the wranglers—but the third and youngest suffered a major peak in anxiety.

As the venison sizzled, a second bear, obviously smaller, sauntered into camp. He stopped and stared which quickly drove the third wrangler over the edge of fear. The two wranglers, relatively unmoved, continued to set up camp. When they rolled out their bedding, the third wrangler grabbed the rifle and with bravado announced that he wasn't that foolish and that he would sit guard...cross-legged...Indian-style...all night long.

In the morning all had earned what they deserved: No bears were shot, two wranglers slept well, no horses were inadvertently destroyed by an over-zealous scared-beyond-reason guardsman, and the now stiff-jointed, bleary-eyed rifleman had given himself the right to convert his fear into self-appointed, self-anointed, altruistic, heroic protectionism.

After the horses were tacked up and just before the rifle was placed back into the scabbard, the head wrangler reloaded it with what had been until then the secretly-removed cartridges.

...More Mountain Ranch Rules...

89. Don't ride the fence line if you can't stretch wire.

90. Don't start a pack trip with anyone who thinks nothin's gonna go wrong.

91. Don't put a slow-minded dude on a quick-minded horse.

92. Don't rope a bull you can't dally up.

93. Don't take the saddle off the rack 'til you've haltered the horse.

94. Don't get used to things going as you think they should.

95. Don't lead your horse to the meadow grass if you're not gonna let him feed.

96. Don't think that scuffin' your dance hall boots makes you a cowboy.

A Sometimes Sing Along...

Sometimes I live in the mountains
Sometimes I live by the sea
And sometimes it seems that all great times
Are there just to smile down at me.

Sometimes the season yells "Springtime"
Sometimes it winks at the trick
And sometimes the snow comes in August
I might have been hopin' too quick.

Sometimes the calves need a brandin'
Sometimes the cows try to run
And sometimes the bulls are a knowin'
That they will be steers when I'm done.

Sometimes my horse says he'll leave me
Sometimes he says that he won't
And sometimes I think he's a good horse
But mostly I think that I don't.

Sometimes my dogs have the good life
Sometimes they suffer with me
And sometimes they wish they were elsewhere
So often I wish that could be.

Sometimes my socks, well, they don't match
Sometimes my shirt it's too small
And sometimes that's life in the mountains
It's make do or don't do at all.

The Chokecherry Concession

Old Bear had learned long ago that all new arriving campers in the canyon would, come morning, fry bacon for breakfast — they always did.

He reminded himself, from his private warm overlook, to be patient, as he had been so many times before — just hunker down and settle in for the night. The notion that for good food "timing is everything," had always held the high ground of reason. No sense making a scene until sunrise when the goods would be on the griddle. And tomorrow, fortunately, would be a morning that he could avoid the long climb to the ridge where breakfast would have consisted of nothing more than the last of the all-too-bitter red chokecherries.

Camper Dad rose in the morning proudly wearing his brand new, incredibly foolish looking "I'm-a-Mountain-Man" hat, and gave to the sunup his best, "Boy, how 'bout that mountain air!" stretch. With his new camping gear still covered with *L. L. Bean* on-sale tags, FedEx labels, and how-to instructions, he started barking out basic-training-style orders as if his sudden self-appointed transformation to wilderness know-it-all deserved the unchallenged quick-step adherence of his troops.

Old Bear had learned during his youthful excursions when he had charged into campsites, the fine art of carefully flipping the campers' hot breakfast skillet into the air. He had also discovered how not to get burned and that airborne bacon cooled fastest of all. The sight of the star spangled splatter of breakfast bacon bursting in air was always beautiful. The sweet smell of Farmer John's finest was more than amazing, but the soon-to-follow uproarious sound of screaming campers racing toward what they thought of as a bear-proof tent, had seemed to him both bothersome and humorous.

The morning campfire started with an eruption — an overdosed volcano, a "more-is-better" mind set of a grenade launching mentality, not the subtle pitch-pine fragrance of a soft start. "Must have been an error in the directions," the boss camper would assure himself. As he used both hands to re-center his hat, he was hopeful that his singed eyebrows would recover before his ineptness suffered critical exposure back at the office.

Old Bear thought this might be more fun than he could have envisioned and, holding one paw over his mouth, tried to hide his giggled impatience.

Victimized and sleepy, both camp family troopers, now helpless subjects of the senior command, rallied slowly to the all-too-loud barking of the camp master's orders. The momma and the kid, dreading some "seize-the-moment nature vs. sleep" speech, pensively rose wanting nothing more than semi-quiet self-protection.

Perhaps, the mom camper contemplated, if he could someday, just once, get an office with a window. Too late now, the latent hunter, the master of the catalogued wilderness experience, laid claim to passion beyond reason.

The caveman-style "kill it and eat it" ads from four-wheel driven Madison Avenue types had taken a too-strong grip. The family circle be dammed and nature beware.

His orders noisily bounced against the fir lined canyon walls: first this, then that, then the other foolish thing. Old Bear rolled on his back and this time all four paws pointed skyward with passive resignation toward the early morning sunlight and again he reminded himself that after coffee comes bacon.

Old Bear relaxed, thinking of the many times he had mentally rehearsed and then passionately displayed his dramatic entrance into camp. Naturally, Old Bear had performed the staged scene with a mighty head toss and widened shoulders, on-hind-legs stance, the mandatory pawing of the air and the obligatory slobbering growl. He wondered if perhaps this time it might be just somewhat over the top; a little too much overacting.

Taking this guy out wouldn't require nearly so much commotion and for once he considered the notion that he should simply play to the crowd and apply only that which would be a sufficient dramatic force.

Old Bear studied the littlest, bleary-eyed camper. Perhaps the small one would get the biggest kick out of watching his dad scramble and whimper. But Old Bear gave a momentary historical mental notice to his fondly remembered youth. He couldn't help but reflect on what seemed to be the not-so-faint memory of his own little cub days. Kids and cubs don't get to pick their parents; they are stuck with the draw, luck or lack thereof.

Old Bear had been perhaps more than just lucky—his folks had been great; and his memories were strong of a joyous youth spent in playful learning. But he had known many other cubs whose fortune had not been so kind. And his personal gratitude carried the burden of somehow acknowledging and in a way sharing the endurance of the painful misfortune of his little cub mates.

"Feeling sorry" for someone always seemed condescending to him; but he felt sorry for them. The others had grown up, or not, without the lessons from their folks, that a cub's life should be safe and fun. He began to notice within himself the cherished sanctity of his sheltered days—and just a small touch of compassion began to emerge for the littlest camper.

Old Bear envisioned that after the breakfast pillage, the little one would one day relate to all his friends and classmates the exciting story of the *Great Bear Adventure!* The drama of the invasion would be hyped and hustled into a brave saga—but long after the public awe had faded away, a son's quiet, sad and private discovery of his dad's fall from grace would remain. Forever locked in his memory would be the dethroning of the magic man, the humiliating never-to-be-revealed cowardice, the shudder of dehumanizing, "Oh Lordy!" panic.

Thinking back to his days as a cub, Old Bear remembered seeing his big bear dad confront and force an even bigger bear to back down. His dad was a hero, and he would always be remembered that way. But now he wondered about the cause and reason behind the opposing bigger bear's subtle glance—in the heat of combat—at him, the littlest cub, just before that much stronger, bigger bear yielded and passively lumbered away.

Maybe the lesson learned was one of needing and having someone to look up to, or to offer up the time—a much needed time—for the little cub to readjust his sights on values. Or maybe compassion with honor is deserved more than earned. Or it could have been something about choosing the right time to win or when it's more than right to take a fall. Or perhaps it was just the thoughtful giving of a much needed opportunity for a little cub to evolve unburdened.

The question still held the floor—the topic unresolved. Is an obvious victory of more value than that which is won by a subtle surrender? Old Bear realized that as a young cub he might have been given a gift. He had been offered up, so it seemed, nothing less than the simple truth: little bears need big bears to look up to.

Realizing that some discoveries take more time and carry more value than others, Old Bear in silent homage to his dad's bigger foe, glanced at the little kid, and slowly resigned himself to move toward the crest away from the campers. There he might find what could be the last of the chokecherries. As he shuffled away, a slight change in the canyon breeze brought the savored, flavored aroma of frying, popping, sizzling bacon.

The littlest camper would not have great stories to tell, and Old Bear wondered if the trauma he had spared him was worth more than the experience they could have shared. He thought, "Come on back someday, little kid, and let's go camping again. I'll show you, when you have learned to yield to another and concede in secret, where the chokecherries hang ripe and clustered the longest... and why they are never really that bitter. If you reach out in a certain respectful manner so as not to harm the branches, you will discover that the flavor and the memories will always return the following year."

It was, in fact, the following year that Old Bear watched as Camper Dad again arrived—his eyebrows having sufficiently healed. He packed now even more of the latest state-of-the-art, high-tech wilderness marvels: cell phone, GPS, and mercifully, this time, a push-button camp stove, a battery-run inflatable mattress, a solar-powered microwave oven, prepackaged firewood glistening in its shrink wrap, and the latest in all other over-the-top doodads no office type could be without.

"Yessiree," Camper Dad hollered, "this is going to be a back-to-nature experience." And he couldn't wait until the moment after camp was set up according to all the explicit directions that he could open the new plastic wrapped box and read the instructions on just how to use this wonderful, fancy, big damn gun.

In the middle of a too-quiet, new moon night, as the campers twisted in their sleeping bags, Old Bear made his way toward the creek to sing and dance with the stand of quaking aspens.

The tall, slender, close-knit trees had, over the years, formed into a perfect bear-back-shaped scratching washboard. He would stand and lean and wiggle, and the aspens would quake against his back. A natural dance would start as he playfully stomped the ground into percussion and rhythm.

He joyfully roared out loud as the trees rubbed his back. He sang bass with passion as his jumping dance steps dislodged massive rolling stones that would whoop and holler and splash their way into the creek. Grateful dead branches would frolic and bash against each other and break into chorus. The trees like back-up singers would shake, rattle and rustle, and the iridescent leaves on top would twist and shout and spark out syncopated treble notes.

The blue jays cheered and piped into the musical commotion squawking alto in siren-like counterpoint. The out-of-tune screech owl loudly reached out for the high notes, he always missed and no one cared. Gray squirrels bantered and chipped in with soprano harmony like two high-speed nickels vibrantly tapped together. The woodpecker duet pounded out staccato riffs, and the kingfisher conductor in long coat tails fought to hold his grip on a wobbly tree-top podium.

It was a high-on-a-mountain performance at the amphitheatre, a blasting trumpet-like natural, mid-night, merry-go-round. Old Bear would wail and snort and howl and swing dance with the aspens. They would tickle his belly and rub his neck and poke at his ears and scratch his butt and kiss his head with soft, bouncing leaves.

The loudest of the big bands played the wondrous hoe-down at the palace of fine trees. It was a life-affirming celebration, a musical turbulence, a fanfare for the common bear. The aspens swayed and held hands and touched shoulders at the dance, a raucous non-moonlight serenade, a tumultuous pandemonium, a melodic riot in an otherwise stillness. A rampaging shatter of the quiet.

The sleepless Camper Dad, whose unsuccessful attempt to zip two sleeping bags together had left him frustrated and frustrated, shivered and sweated in bone-chilling fear at the all-too-near thunderous "earth-is-ending" chaos. Terror and trauma to the tenth power tore at his throat.

He cowered at the explosive, branch-breaking, hard-rock-bashing, echoing roar of what he dreaded must be a demon Big Foot on attack, a pre-historic bulldozer battling back at a landslide, some kind of brutal, savage "death is imminent" assault of a giant dinosaur, a psychic paralyzer.

—Stop, Stop! Just Make It Stop!
—Stop The Roar —Stop All The Roars!
—The Gun —Of Course, The Big Damn Gun!

He fired at the god-awful noise.

—Just Fire — Keep firing! Again, Again, and Again!
—Stop The Earthquake, Stop The Life-Threatening Fright — Just Make It Stop!

First the blast and the recoil scared the hell out of him. Then the echo of the rifle shots and the screams from his "What the ...!!" family put the hell back in him.

The bullets ripped and tore, slammed and ricocheted. Soon, blocked by the roar in his head, he couldn't hear that all was quiet.

The dance was over.

His nostrils recoiled from the unfamiliar acidic stench of gunfire.

Nothing moved but the screaming echoes and the wetness down the front of his plaid pajamas.

In the mad-panic, scared-to-death, rush to outrun his own horrible demons, some of his pricey camp gear, now quickly wadded and flung, actually made it into his cute SUV.

His door-slamming, high-speed getaway left behind most of his treasured wilderness equipment marking his disregard for the concept of "pack-it-in, pack-it-out." He intentionally left the memory-filled camera.

Camper Dad's car was mangled during his wheel-spinning, headlight-breaking, fender-bashing lunge down the narrow tree-tunneled logging spur away from the mountains. Camper Kid, in his underwear and his disbelief, bounced and launched and banged his head hard against the car ceiling. Mom gripped the dash and lost grip on reality. He raced for the sanity of the suburbs.

He had gone too far into an unknown world and had found himself up against the unexpected edge of his own brutal, mad-making wilderness. And it was now too late for him to ever make sense of the inconceivable distance and savage conflict between his unwarranted perception and reality.

It was later that season when the chokecherries had ripened and by then Old Bear should have surely made his way to the ridge, that the lonely warm-hearted summer graciously, silently, offered up and surrendered the mountains to autumn.

The too-heavy fruit laden branches finally broke to the ground and not too soon after the late winter snows, came spring and a chokecherry—only one, so it seemed, cautiously took to seed.

As time passed, the spreading runners of the squaw-blanket plants deliberately crept over and buried the rusted, rotted rifle.

Still many years later, just as had been true for all the years since, the blue jays meet on the ridge during the start of the camping season. They draw straws to see who, among the most accurate, would continue the traditional loving memory of their beloved buddy, Old Bear.

The winner earned the privilege of delivering, with overhead, high powered, pinpoint center-of-the-skillet precision, the all-naturally-processed chokecherry-flavored bacon seasoning.

...More Mountain Ranch Rules...

97. Don't think your best horse won't sometimes put your butt in the air.

98. Don't start a pack trip without knowing you brought something you won't need and left at the barn something you will.

99. Don't think the trail you rode yesterday is gonna look the same today.

100. Don't let a dude night wrangle with a loaded rifle.

101. Don't lock your feet in the stirrups if God hasn't told you "It's O.K."

102. Don't think a saddle that started tightly cinched will stay that way.

103. Don't think that your highly paid professional wilderness guide always knows exactly where he's going.

104. Don't think the inside of a man hasn't got a lot to do with the outside of a horse, the far side of a mountain, the good side of a woman and the top side of a dream.

...And Sometimes...

Sometimes that girl says she loves me
Sometimes she says that she won't
And sometimes I get into trouble
Then wish that it was that I don't.

Sometimes my truck thinks it will start
Sometimes it knows that ain't true
And sometimes I glare at the big sky
'Cause answers come too far and few.

Sometimes the river runs with me
Sometimes it just flows uphill
And sometimes I stare into heaven
It's "won't" that I want less than "will."

Sometimes the hills tell a story
Sometimes I hear with my heart
And sometimes the best of the good time
Is hardly much more than a start.

Sometimes my best gal's a real bitch
Sometimes she'll holler and yell
And sometimes when I know she's just right
She tells me to go straight to hell.

Sometimes the big stars shine so clear
Sometimes trees hold the moonlight
And sometimes the river reminds me
I better stay with her tonight.

The Gift

The lovely lady from Lake Calaveras knew that this birthday was going to be a hard one for the old guy. One of those "Have I still got it?" milestones.

She was a "Show, Don't Tell" kind of woman who knew that this time, somehow, more was required than just consoling words and encouragement. Any attempt to find a gift might be the impossible challenge.

He just needed that hint of self-doubt to be banished and his youthful manliness re-affirmed.

At the gas station, she overheard two foolish hooligans discussing their dilemma. They counted their change and turned out their pockets and whined and pouted about the high cost of fuel.

It was a "scales-of-finance" balancing act, weighing the need but not having the funds for both gas and beer. They deliberated the merits of one or the other: the gas without beer or beer without gas.

With a ridiculous palms-up-tipping-scales demonstration, one attempted to explain his theory of supply and demand as the other gleefully discovered under the seat, a crumpled, insufficient, almost pre-digested dollar bill.

The calamity escalated as each young punk began to blame the other for their predicament.

"This will do," she thought as she approached them. She explained how they could have both the gas and the beer. She reviewed with them the fine points of how to siphon gas from an old unsuspecting truck owner. She provided them with directions to the old man's house and told them to time it for right at midnight when he would be asleep.

Saying nothing more than, "Here, this is for the old man," she scribbled a note, sealed it in a little envelope and stuffed it into one of the buffoon's shirt pockets. Soon they were concentrating on the beer they had bought with the gas money and impatiently waiting for midnight. Curiously, they agreed not to immediately break into and read the private note but to save it for later when they would share the laugh with others and probably figure out just what it was the lady seemed to have against the old man anyway.

The solitary man marked his birthday at the stroke of 12 o'clock. The house was dark except for the lone candle on the Twinkie as he carefully, ceremoniously blew out the flame on his fifties.

He toasted himself with a mocking, "Well, I made it this far..." in sing-song tempo with the proper melody befitting the occasion. Just as he lifted the one-bite-birthday-cake from the over-sized platter, he heard some small sound in his driveway which prompted him to investigate.

His tight grip on the throats of both thieves caused their facial color to advance from scared white to toes-just-touching-the-ground magenta. The siphon hose now hung limply and the gas can, still at the ready, giggled, pointed at, and incriminated the levitating suspects.

Enjoying the capture and resultant rediscovery of the surprising strength in his taut arms he slowly, with calculated precision, siphoned the energy right out of them. He calmly explained to the quivering, choking duo his heart-felt convictions about the concept of private property and attempted theft. He intentionally let his ever-so-slow speech meander and digress and last more than long enough to assure himself that his hand-delivered, throat-clutching fear had found a home.

His arms felt like steel and the pounding in his chest was thrilling. He was strong, he was capable and he stood tall and nothing ached or creaked as he continued to tighten his grasp on the knowledge that he was still young enough.

One of the thieves — now turned victim and now on the verge of wetting his pants — remembered and cautiously offered up the lady's envelope.

The trembling, quaking young fools, whose sputtering lives were about to pass out before their very eyes were now too afraid and exhausted to move. They were baffled and somewhat relieved by the slight smile on the old man's face as he silently read to himself:

"Happy Birthday,
Much love,
The lady from Lake Calaveras"

...More Mountain Ranch Rules...

105. Don't think a horse's gentle eye gives a clue about his black heart.

106. Don't think you're the first rider to have to rinse out his underwear in a creek.

107. Don't think your horse won't sometimes balance himself on your foot.

108. Don't believe most who say "Can ride, rope and rodeo" have done more than think about it.

109. Don't believe a spooky horse can't swap ends in a heart beat.

110. Don't get on a horse in a corral if you're not gonna be able to get back on him in the mountains.

111. Don't build a corral with rails on the outside of the post if you want horses to stay on the inside.

112. Don't waste time trying to find a horse with no faults unless you're a person with no faults.

...And the Critics Rave

11. This University has ruled in Mr. Bianco's favor. *Finding the "Why" in Graeagle* is clear and convincing evidence that he should be granted a full refund of monies spent on bonehead English.

The University Board of Regents

12. At the author's last "Publish and Perish" staff meeting I, and others, spoke to the affirmative on the topic: "Is this book really that bad?"

Cowboy Bill

13. Campers have found the pages of this book to be extremely helpful for starting their fireside literary discussions.

The Graeagle Volunteer Fire Department

14. Journey through frolicking bunk-filled excursions that have no merit, no redeeming value and no social consciousness. His stories have the wit and charm of a DMV courtesy manual.

Bret

15. We don't get it. . .

The Portola Reporter

16. After reviewing Mr. Bianco's manuscript I can, without reservation, make assurances that there is no foundation for the legal challenges of libel, slander, defamation of character, malice or factual impropriety.

Signed: Anonymous, Attorney at Law

. . . More Mountain Ranch Rules

113. Don't sit at the poker table if you don't know who the sucker is.

114. Don't think you're the first to make the mistake of reading trail sign straight into the devil's maze.

115. Don't hold her hand if she doesn't hold your heart.

116. Don't forget to save time to dance out in the moonlight.

117. Don't think you're not worth an ever-loving thing.

118. Don't ever think it's O.K. not to love.

119. Don't think these rules are subject to change.

120. Don't think your trail boss is obliged to explain all these rules.

And, Don't think you can't find the "Why" in Graeagle.

The Fixer-Upper

The small historic mountain town, seemingly buried in the tall pine forest, had the usual array of over decorated shops selling the usual over priced gifts.

The shops carried a not-so-intriguing assortment of "designer" items for the home, most of which were the universally accepted, made-in-China trinkets that had long since replaced anything of local character, craftsmanship or value.

But one shop was different.

More by accident than intent, some unknowing visitors occasionally wandered into the tiny shop labeled nothing more than "Art."

The sign proclaiming "Art" was so sorely in need of paint that it appeared the message was in conflict with the medium.

It was easy to imagine that some might have thought the sign referred to a name, perhaps the current or previous owner. Others may have envisioned a folklore "legend of Art" or maybe "Art" was a plaintive notice to a long lost soul who might yield to the beckoning, stumble in, and explain just where in the hell he had been. "Art, come home—all is forgiven."

Simply, the old disheveled, cramped shop sold art and supplies for artists. Everything from hard-to-pronounce colors in tiny tubes to foot-wide brushes for white washing fences. Homemade easels leaned against a rack of paint rollers. "How-To" and "How-To-

Un-Do" and "How-To-Re-Do" books encircled a mixed assortment of out-of-order, faded paint color chips.

Some lodgepole framed water color paintings of leaning barns by L.A. Cross hung at random within the store. Pencil sketches of the Gold Rush era by George Mathis seemed to be more than comfortable hiding in the clutter as if surrounded and protected by old friends.

A few black and white photographs in flat black frames appeared like salt and pepper throughout the never-really-thought-out decor of the shop.

The little store was a step-over, walk-around, watch-out-for-that, traffic-flow, human-engineering, ergonomic nightmare. There was no tell-tale indicator of a too-well-executed professional marketing firm on site. But those few who came in seemed to enjoy the natural chaos.

"Art" was the store: the sum of more than just its ingredients, yet it offered nothing more or less than the sign stated.

No one seemed to notice — and no one seemed to care — that the lady who entered the store was the first and, in fact, only customer in three or more days. It could have been because no one else was there.

Though most assuredly she was from out of town, and definitely this was her first time in the store, she maneuvered through the clutter and disorder with a simple, graceful ease. Her eyes could see the fun and beauty as her feet avoided the pitfalls.

She had over-the-shoulder sun-streaked chestnut hair, a summer dress with a subtle flower print and thin bow-tied straps, and wispy sandals. She looked as if she felt she was barefoot. It appeared that her gentle nature fit well into the store, as if somehow she recognized within herself something familiar inside and out, and at the same time, new and unknown.

She delicately gazed, with honor-laden respect, at the seemingly chaotic collection of art. Her perceptive, tender glance flowed from subject to subject as she eased through the maze to appreciate each work of art without judging it — just a soft mental tasting.

It was near the back of the store — although front from back was hard to distinguish — that she came upon another of the many black and white photographs. This one was slightly larger than the others and also encased in the standard, very black, very simple frame.

She stopped and both feet seemed to find a home. Her soft gaze slowly transformed into an absolute, straight-ahead stare. The photograph gripped her like gravity.

It was a simple photo of a snow-covered stone chimney. Well, not just the chimney, but all of it: the fireplace, the hearth, the mantle and the chimney--all made of stone and all covered in snow. The log cabin that must have watched over it was long since gone. The solitary fireplace and its chimney still stood, a stone cold barren remnant and reminder of what once must have been: a warmth, a life, now gone.

Seated in the black and white contrast of the chimney and the snow, on the massive platform of the hearth, was a man, his face hidden by the head-down tilt of his cowboy hat. His elbows on his knees seemed to support his slumping, weary soul. It did not appear that he had brushed the snow away before he sat down, but rather that he had just resigned himself to sit in the snow. His snow covered hat and forearms told that he had been there awhile. The chimney and the solitary man shared the cold and the stones and the snow and the moment.

She wondered what else they might have had in common. And she wondered if anyone else had noticed that over the man's shoulder, in the early morning sky, was the hopeful beacon of a faint daylight full moon. She saw in small letters the penciled title partially hidden and smudged in the lower right corner: "The Fixer-Upper."

She now felt an overwhelming need to learn more about the "The Fixer-Upper," but no one was in the store. Although she had cherished her exploration of the small town, her plans had not been to stay for a second day in anticipation of finding someone there.

But she did stay — and the next day she watched "Art" from across the street during morning coffee at the cafe. There did not seem to be a "Closed" sign and she doubted if there would be an "Open."

During yesterday's discovery at the store, she had seen no one and wondered if there really was someone, anyone, who ran the shop. Perhaps it was one of those old-fashioned "help yourself, take-what-you-need, put-your-money-or-your-marker-in-the-box" kind of places.

She wanted to meet the shop owner. She wanted "The Fixer-Upper."

Near the end of her second cup of coffee, she watched as a tall, lanky man wearing Levis and cowboy boots launched himself up the three wooden steps to the front door of "Art."

He entered without a key. Without any other reason it seemed to her that "Art" might now be "Open."

As he hung his cowboy hat on a wall peg, she ran up the steps and entered the store. She greeted him and inquired about "The Fixer-Upper."

His words came carefully, patiently, almost solemnly and were worth a thousand pictures directing and diverting her toward the other black and white photos that could be purchased.

One that he referred her to showed the back of the man with the cowboy hat, his saddle slung over his shoulder, as he walked away toward a distant tree line. A second one had caught the cowboy standing, leaning against the side of a barn, arms folded, and legs crossed. His hat was tipped down so that again no face appeared.

Only by his soft inference did she begin to perceive that perhaps a strong connection had bound this gentle man to the meaningful photograph.

She knew that the photo had captured far more than a moment, perhaps the connection between two parallel lives. And she hoped for the restart of one, not just the end of both.

On a course to learn what fate had dealt the man, she quietly asked first what had become of the old chimney.

He began to fidget with the stray papers on the counter that suddenly held some new unwarranted value. An inadvertent and indiscernible cautious re-grip of the pencil accompanied his reluctant explanation that not too long after the photo had been taken, the old chimney had finally, violently tumbled. It had become the victim of a massive collapse of a twisted, coreless, windblown tree with rotted gray roots.

His glance eased away. His wary nature surfaced as he hoped to avoid the next question.

She didn't ask.

Later that afternoon, the little cow bell over the door startled the napping clerk at the small inn at the edge of town. The gentle lady's request brought another surprise. It had been a long time since anyone had stayed for a second night. Tourists always seem to make all of their discoveries about the little town in just one day.

There was something different about the quiet lady.

The innkeeper watched her go out the door and, with cordial regard, gave an approving nod to no one after seeing that the lady's light steps towards the cottage seem to quicken and become almost child-like as if ushered by some new awareness.

The gentle lady held the key and this time she noticed the homey welcoming feel of the soft leather fob with the small words branded: "Outside Inn."

As she walked down the graveled and pine-needled path, she felt caressed by a lofting, smiling notion that perhaps she just might, with a warm, open hand, hold the key to a long-locked door.

...And Sometimes

Sometimes the trees stand me shelter
Sometimes I'm whisperin' cold
And sometimes the camp fire reminds me
I've got more than plenty to hold.

Sometimes the city ain't that bad
Sometimes it's worse than I thought
And sometimes I note my good fortune
At lessons this small town has taught.

Sometimes the fish are a jumpin'
Sometimes they're hunkerin' down
And sometimes the message is simple
Graeagle's just that kind of town.

Sometimes the trail is a windin'
Sometimes it's mine for to roam
And sometimes asit the front porch swing
I know that I've found me a home.

Sometimes I say what I'm thinking
Sometimes I stand back and look
And sometimes I think I will write it
America's worst selling book.

Sometimes the "When" just ain't right now
Sometimes the "How" ain't legal
And sometimes the "Where" and "What" hide out
But I found the "Why" in Graeagle.

"... and the more I grope about the muddy water for a glimmer I have glimpsed, the muddier the water becomes and the less likely it seems that I shall grasp it."

Vladimir Nabokov
1899-1977

To order copies of :

Finding the "Why" in Graeagle

Whimsical Mountain Tales and Shameless Lies...

Please write or call:

Paul Bianco
P.O. Box 1001
Graeagle, CA 96103

530-836-0539

$14.95 each plus $3.00 shipping & handling for the first book and $1.00 shipping & handling for each additional book.